HUMAN GENETICS
Principles and Methods

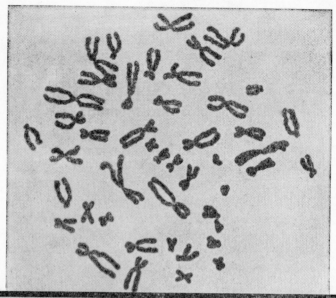

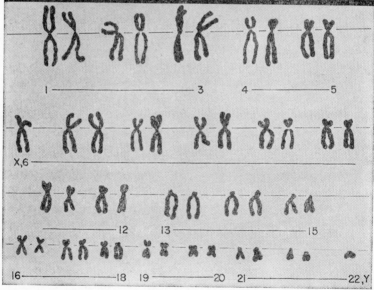

Karyotype of Normal Human Male (× 2,100).

The preparation was made from peripheral blood according to a method modified from Moorhead, et al., Experimental Cell Research 20:613, September, 1960. Courtesy of Niel Wald, M. D., Graduate School of Public Health, and Wayne Borges, M. D., Children's Hospital, University of Pittsburgh.

HUMAN GENETICS

Principles and Methods

Ching Chun Li, Ph.D.

Professor of Biometry,
Graduate School of Public Health,
University of Pittsburgh

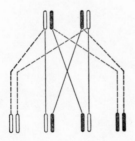

The Blakiston Division
McGraw-Hill Book Company
New York   Toronto   London

HUMAN GENETICS: PRINCIPLES AND METHODS

Library of Congress Catalog Card Number: 61-9771

II

37700

Preface

Human genetics is no longer, if it ever has been, something that can be covered in a compact one-semester course, taught by one teacher, using one textbook. It involves so many widely different disciplines that no single person can master them all. Clinical and biochemical studies of the hereditary diseases represent one phase of human genetics, immunologic studies represent another, and the physiologic and psychologic studies still another. There are detailed compilations of family pedigrees, there are epidemiologic studies of relatives, there are investigations into the association between hereditary traits and diseases, and there are the high-power microscopic examinations of human chromosomes. Some geneticists are trying to use our present knowledge to interpret human evolution and to speculate on its future course, while others are content merely with the estimation of mutation rates of some known loci. Some may be concerned with the genetic differences between an African population and a Southern European population, and others may be concerned merely about the difference in hair color between a mother and her daughter. All of this is good human genetics.

This book is an outgrowth of my notes for a short, fifteen-lecture course in human genetics that I have taught for the last several years in the Graduate School of Public Health at the University of Pittsburgh. The content is designed to provide material of general interest and value to a highly heterogeneous group of students, ranging from physicians who have barely heard of Mendel's law, to graduate students in biology who are doing

v

active research in population genetics. Because of this fact, there
is no review of the literature on any particular subject and no detailed descriptions of hereditary diseases. Rather than use such
descriptions as the central subject of discussion, I have employed
them as examples to illustrate certain principles. By this technique, I have tried to explain some basic principles which will
serve as a foundation for further understanding and study.

A clinical biochemist wonders why the Mendelian ratio cannot
be calculated directly from his painstakingly collected pedigrees;
an expert in heart disease wonders why a simple dominant gene
cannot be assumed with certainty when the disease is scattered
over three generations. A hematologist, unable to distinguish
the heterozygous from the homozygous mother through biochemical tests, may turn for a magic answer to a geneticist, as if
he were able to see the hemophilia genes. An intelligent layman
or a scientist in some other field may not understand why continued selection against a certain hereditary disease does not
eradicate it from the population. Many people, apparently, still
believe that a gene, especially a gene for disease, once imported
from outside will spread throughout the population. That a gene
for intelligence, similarly imported, does not increase in frequency
at all, does not seem to be contradictory to this belief. Normal-
ity is dominant; harmfulness is recessive; and that is that. Many
people, including a small number of geneticists, either still believe
that genetic linkage leads to association of the genetic traits,
or they are very vague and uncertain about the relationship.
On the one hand, there is the prediction that in a few thousand
years man will be all brain and no muscle, and, on the other hand,
there is fear that man's intelligence has been declining because
of the higher fertility of the low intelligence groups who may have
muscle. Many of these misunderstandings or half-understand-
ings stem from an inadequate appreciation of the basic principles
in population genetics. While I cannot hope for a short book to
dispel all these misbeliefs, I do hope to correct some of them.

A special effort has been made to introduce the concept of
genetic equilibrium. Truly, without an equilibrium mechanism,
human beings and the entire biologic world would be in chaos.
Heredity is a conservative force in nature. The stability of the

genetic composition of a population must be understood first, if we are to study change.

The objection has often been made that the description of genetic principles and methods usually involves too much mathematics and statistics for general students in medicine or biology. The complaint is honest and valid to various degrees, depending on the subject matter. This book is limited to very basic principles, and mathematics has been reduced to a bare minimum. In many instances the algebraic expressions and numerical values are put side by side, so that no one can honestly complain that he does not understand q^2. In other instances the algebraic approach has been omitted altogether, and the entire presentation is based on a suitable numerical example. Academically minded people may not agree with the numerical method because it loses the "generality," but I find it most efficient, both as a means of learning and as a tool of teaching. If the choice is between the general and the numerical, I choose the general. If the choice is between the numerical and none, I choose the numerical.

I have made a special effort to keep this book as small as possible. There are no drill exercises at the end of the chapters, but there are some hidden exercises intermixed with text. When I use a certain calculation procedure to obtain certain values, the reader is advised to go through the same procedure to obtain a similar value or the next one in the sequence. In so doing, he will undoubtedly pick up the details and gain understanding. He will soon discover that the mathematics that used to block him may disappear at the point of a reasonably determined pencil.

The list of references has also been reduced to a minimum. When an author has several papers on more or less the same subject, usually only one or two are chosen. A paper may be cited for its historical importance, for its general interest, for its simplicity, or because it represents a new development. However, for each reference cited there are probably ten others equally relevant to the subject matter under consideration. The omissions are due to the author's ignorance and desire for brevity and does not reflect on the importance of the work.

The first chapter, dealing with Mendelian law of inheritance, is included only for the sake of completeness, thus making the book self-contained. The second chapter deals with a fundamental law for a random-mating population; it is a prerequisite for the rest of the book. The subsequent chapters need not necessarily be read in sequence. In fact, some of them may be read independently according to the need and interest of the reader.

I am most grateful to Professor Antonio Ciocco who first conceived the idea of giving a short course in human genetics dealing with the fundamental principles. With warm personal interest and constant encouragement he has also provided general guidance to the development of the course.

C. C. Li

Contents

Chapter 1

The Family Laws

Genetics is the science of heredity; and human genetics is largely an application of genetic principles and methods to the study of human heredity. However, there are many considerations and situations that are unique to man. It is the purpose of this book to expound the fundamental principles in heredity and some of the methods specially developed to deal with human data. Reversing the sequence of historical development, we shall first give a sketch of the physical mechanism of heredity.

Cytologic Facts

In the nucleus of human somatic cells there are normally 23 *pairs* of chromosomes (Tjio and Levan, 1956; Ford and Hamerton, 1956). One of these pairs is called the *sex chromosomes*, designated as X and Y, and the remaining 22 pairs are *autosomes*. To save verbal description, a photomicrograph of such chromosomes (Wald and Borges, 1960) has been reproduced in the frontispiece. The autosomes have been numbered according to their length, the first pair being the longest and the twenty-second the shortest. The two members of a pair are the same length and are made of the same genetic material. They are said to be *homologous* to each other. The pair of sex chromosomes is, however, heteromorphic, the X being approximately five times as long as the Y. The reader will notice in the photomicrograph that each chromosome is (faintly visible) split lengthwise into two halves. The halves are called *chromatids*, held together by a *centromere*, which appears as a constriction (or blank) in the picture. The centromere thus divides a chromosome into two "arms." The ratio of the length of

1

the two "arms," together with the total length, enables us to identify the various pairs of chromosomes in a well-prepared slide.

When a somatic cell divides, each chromosome splits lengthwise into two separate halves: one chromatid goes to one daughter cell and the other chromatid goes to the other daughter cell, so the two daughter cells are exactly the same in chromosomal content and each has 46 chromosomes, like the mother cell. This type of cell division, known as *mitosis*, is purely multiplicative in nature: one cell divides into two. It increases the number of cells without changing the chromosomal number or content. This type of cell division will not be discussed further.

The germ or reproductive cells (sperms and eggs) are, however, produced in a different and more involved manner. In the gonads (testis and ovary) a mother cell with 23 pairs of chromosomes goes through a dividing process by which the daughter cells (sperms or eggs) receive only *one member of each pair* of the chromosomes. This type of cell division is known as reduction division, or *meiosis*. A detailed cytologic description of meiosis is unnecessary here. Briefly, immediately before reduction division, the two member chromosomes (partners) of each pair move together side by side with each other, a process known as *synapsis*. After synapsis, each member or partner of a pair goes to a different daughter cell, so each mature reproductive cell has only 23 single chromosomes without their corresponding partners. The process can be symbolized as follows (prime signs to distinguish the partners):

Mother cell: $\{1,1'; 2,2'; \cdots ; 21, 21'; 22, 22'; X,Y\}$ = 23 pairs
Gamete: $\{\ 1;\ \ 2';\ \cdots\ ;\ \ 21';\ \ \ 22;\ \ \ \ X\}$ = 23 singles

Of the first pair $(1,1')$ of chromosomes in the mother cell, either 1 or $1'$ may go to a particular daughter cell. The same is true of 2, $2'$ and every other pair. In the symbolization, one germ cell is shown as an example. The separation of 1 and $1'$ into two germ cells is independent of the separation of 2 and $2'$, and so on. The fact that the partners of each pair separate independently of the other pairs is known as *independent assortment*. Hence, for any given mother cell, there are $2 \times 2 \times 2 \times \cdots \times 2 = 2^{23} = 8,388,608$

equally possible types of germ cells as far as whole chromosomes are concerned. This seemingly large number of possibilities is, however, a gross understatement of the true picture, when we consider the very many genes located on each chromosome and the mutual exchange of homologous portions between the chromosome partners during the period of synapsis.

As each sperm or egg has a set (a *genome*) of 23 single chromosomes, when a sperm fertilizes an egg, the resulting *zygote* has again 23 pairs of chromosomes. A reproductive cell with one set of $n = 23$ single chromosomes is said to be *haploid*. An individual, resulting from the union of two germ cells, has two sets, or $2n = 2 \times 23 = 46$ chromosomes, and is said to be *diploid*. Summing up, a halving process (meiosis) precedes a union process (fertilization); not only does the somatic number of chromosomes remain constant throughout generations, but the genes and chromosomes are thoroughly shuffled in each generation. Such is the ingenuity of Nature.

Genes and Chromosomes

Through thousands of well-designed experiments with plants and animals since 1900, it has been proved beyond doubt that the basic organic units controlling heredity are located on the chromosomes. These units are called *genes*. Genes are linearly arranged along the length of the chromosomes. The location of a gene on the chromosome is called a *locus*. The exact number of loci on a chromosome is unknown, but there are presumably thousands of them on each chromosome. Genes are submicroscopic in size and cannot be observed directly, but they can be studied through their effects on the organism by making certain types of crosses. From the cytologic description in the preceding section, it is clear that all an offspring inherits from his parents are the two chromosome sets, one set from the mother and one from the father. The cytoplasmic influence on heredity is not discussed in this book. It is these two sets of chromosomes (as gene carriers) that determine the heredity of an individual. Chromosomes may be visualized as vehicles by which the genes are transmitted from parent to offspring.

For our present purpose we may still regard a gene as a discrete and indivisible unit on a chromosome, and the detailed structure and composition of a gene need not concern us. However, owing to recent and refined analysis of genetic experiments, the concept of gene structure has been modified considerably, and a few passing remarks may not be entirely out of place. Briefly, the gene may not be the ultimate unit of organization or function but may consist of several simpler subunits or bands or sites, each of which may undergo changes. These have been called *mutational sites*. There is probably no structural differentiation between the genes and the chromosome. The chromosome is merely regarded as a linear sequence of sites (building blocks) of only a few different kinds, and a particular ordered arrangement (permutation) of some of these sites determines a particular function: a *cistron* (a gene effect). In other words, the old concept is that a gene is like an ideographic Chinese character, and the current concept is that a gene is rather like an English word: a permutation of a limited number of letters.

One Autosomal Locus

It should be realized from the cytologic description that it is an impossible task to study all the genes on all the chromosomes at the same time. The secret of Mendel's success in discovering basic laws of heredity is that he concentrated on one simple character at a time and followed it through two or more generations. In human genetics we are still using essentially the methodology of Mendel in this respect, only replacing controlled crosses by observation of family pedigrees. It is this change of tactics that requires some special statistical techniques for appropriate analyses. This subject is taken up in a later chapter.

We shall first concentrate on a certain locus on one of the 22 pairs of autosomes. If every gene on this locus in the entire population is identical with every other on the same locus, there is no way, or need, to study this locus because these genes are omnipresent in every individual. It is the difference in gene effect that we can and shall study. Now let us assume that there are two alternate forms to the gene of the locus under consideration, and let us call them A and A'. That means, the form A gene has a certain effect (say, normal pigmentation or normal hemoglobin) and the form A' has a different effect (say, lack of pigmentation or abnormal hemoglobin). The two forms, A and A', are called the *alleles* of this particular locus. If we imagine that A is located on chromosome 1 and A' on chromosome 1', then the transmission of these genes from parent to offspring follows the same pattern described for the chromosomes. An individual may assume one of three possible types with respect to this locus, viz., AA, AA', or A'A'. These are called the *genotypes* of individuals with respect to this locus. The genotypes AA and A'A' are called *homozygotes*, because the two member genes are of the same form; genotype AA' is a *heterozygote*.

If each allele has a separate recognizable effect independent of that of the other allele, then there will be three distinguishable types of individuals. For example, AA individuals have all normal hemoglobins; AA' individuals have 60 per cent normal and 40 per cent abnormal hemoglobins; and A'A' individuals have all abnormal hemoglobins. These are the three *phenotypes* corresponding to the three genotypes. However, it often happens that the heterozygote AA' is indistinguishable from one of the homozygotes, say, AA. Then we say that the allele A is *dominant* over A', or that A' is *recessive* to A. In such a case, AA and AA' will be of one phenotype and A'A' of another, and there will be only two phenotypes. In fact, the heterozygote AA' may assume a type anywhere intermediate between those of AA and A'A'. So we see that dominance is a matter of degree as well as a matter of detection. One of the preoccupations in human genetics is to refine the detecting methods by which the heterozygotes may be distinguished from the dominant homozygotes. When there is dominance, the capital A is used to designate the dominant allele and the lower-case a (instead of A'), the recessive. The traditional A, a symbolism is used in the following paragraphs for its convenience, even though dominance is not necessarily implied.

Mendelian Inheritance

Each of the three genotypes AA, Aa, aa may be a male or a female. The problem of sex will be dealt with in the latter part of this chapter. Here, the gametes refer to sperms in the case of a male and to eggs in the case of a female. The gametes produced by the various genotypes are as follows:

Individual AA produces 100 per cent A gametes;

Individual Aa produces 50 per cent A gametes and 50 per cent a gametes;

Individual aa produces 100 per cent a gametes.

Similarly, ignoring sex, the cross (mating or marriage) AA × Aa stands for mother AA × father Aa or the reciprocal cross father AA × mother Aa, since these two types of mating yield the same results (children). A child results from the union of two gametes, one from each parent. The method of obtaining the genotypes of children and calculating the proportions among them from a given mating may be exemplified by considering the results of Aa × aa and Aa × Aa.

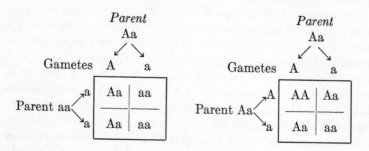

The mating Aa × aa produces 50 per cent Aa and 50 per cent aa children; and the mating Aa × Aa produces 25 per cent AA, 50 per cent Aa, and 25 per cent aa children. These results are based on the tacit assumption that any gamete of one parent is equally likely to unite with any gamete of the other parent. That this assumption is by and large true is borne out by numerous experimental results in plants and animals as well as by observational data on man. The percentages described above may also be expressed in the form of *ratios*. Thus, among the children of Aa × Aa parents, the ratio is 1AA:2Aa: 1aa, or 1:2:1 for short. Furthermore, if A is dominant over a so AA and Aa have the same phenotype, the ratio of the dominant children to the recessives would be

3:1. This is probably the best known and most celebrated classic Mendelian ratio, the symbol of modern genetics.

There being three genotypes with respect to the A,a autosomal locus, there are altogether six possible mating types without distinguishing between reciprocal crosses. Two of the more important ones have been studied in the preceding paragraph, but for the sake of completeness and later reference all the six mating types and their children are listed in Table 1-1. These Mendelian

TABLE 1-1. FAMILY LAWS FOR AUTOSOMAL GENES

Parents (mating types)	Probability of Offspring		
	AA	Aa	aa
AA × AA	1	0	0
AA × Aa	½	½	0
Aa × Aa	¼	½	¼
AA × aa	0	1	0
Aa × aa	0	½	½
aa × aa	0	0	1

laws may be called the *family laws* because they apply to specified types of families. There may be millions of families in a human population. If one asks which of these mating types are common and which are rare, the question is beyond the scope of the family laws and cannot be answered at this stage. All the Mendelian law says is that, if the two parents are such and such, we would expect certain kinds of children in certain proportions, and that is all. The questions concerning a population will be dealt with in the next chapter.

Pedigrees and Probabilities

The family laws listed in Table 1-1 are so fundamental in the study of heredity that they have been translated into the form of *idealized pedigrees* (Fig. 1-1). "Idealized" is used in contradistinction to "typical" for several reasons. In the first place, a family does not necessarily have four children. Second, even when a family (say, Aa × Aa) has four children, they are not necessarily 1AA + 2Aa + 1aa, as depicted in the diagram. In fact, all possible types of sibships ranging from four AA to four aa will occur and only 18–19 per cent of such Aa × Aa families will be expected to obtain the ideal segregation (see below). Nevertheless, these diagrams serve some useful purposes. At one glance, they sum-

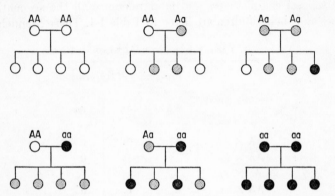

FIG. 1-1. The six types of families with respect to one pair of autosomal genes. The sex of the individuals is *not* indicated and the reciprocal cross is *not* distinguished. Thus, in the mating Aa × aa, either genotype may be the father or the mother. Plain circle = homozygote AA; solid circle = homozygote aa; stippled circle = heterozygote Aa. In case of dominance we may ignore the stippling and regard it as indistinguishable from the plain circles.

marize the Mendelian law and show the various possibilities for each type of family. In an actual study, a pedigree may involve more than 100 persons extending over several generations. No matter how extensive and complicated a pedigree is, it can always be broken down into the six basic types of family units with respect to monofactorial inheritance. A large pedigree is simply a conglomeration of the elementary family units connected through marriages.

As might have been noticed, the first attempt to smuggle the concept of probability into the Mendelian law is that the word *probability* appeared in the title of Table 1-1 in place of the word *proportion*. Plant geneticists can get along very well without ever using the word *probability* because they are dealing with very

large families in which the expected Mendelian ratios are usually
well realized; to them the word *proportion* is quite sufficient. In
human genetics, however, the concept of probability is indis-
pensable, even when dealing with very simple problems. Unfortunately, any systematic treatment of the probability concept will
carry us well beyond the scope of this book. As a compromise, the
student may review the chapter on probability in any algebra
textbook and then work out the concrete case of Aa × Aa families
with four children, given in the following paragraph. Or the
reader may skip the following paragraph in the first reading, as a
similar problem will be dealt with in Chap. 5.

If the Aa × Aa parents have only one child, the a priori proba-
bility that the child be AA, Aa, or aa is $\frac{1}{4}$, $\frac{1}{2}$, or $\frac{1}{4}$, respectively.
After birth, he can be only one of the three genotypes, of course.
The genotype of this child does not influence that of a second
child, and we say that each childbirth is an *independent event*.
The probabilities for the second child are also $\frac{1}{4}$AA, $\frac{1}{2}$Aa, and
$\frac{1}{4}$aa. Hence, for families with two children, the probability of the
various types of sib pairs is given by the terms of the product

$$(\tfrac{1}{4}AA + \tfrac{1}{2}Aa + \tfrac{1}{4}aa)(\tfrac{1}{4}AA + \tfrac{1}{2}Aa + \tfrac{1}{4}aa)$$
$$= (\tfrac{1}{4}AA + \tfrac{1}{2}Aa + \tfrac{1}{4}aa)^2$$

If we ignore the order of birth and simply count the *number* of the
various genotypes, then the sib pair "first AA, second aa" and
the pair "first aa, second AA" may be considered of the same
type (combination): one AA and one aa. Similarly, if there are
four children, the probability of the various types (combinations
of siblings) is given by the terms of $(\frac{1}{4}AA + \frac{1}{2}Aa + \frac{1}{4}aa)^4$. To
expand this expression, no formula or mathematical knowledge
is required other than longhand multiplication. To make the
simple multiplication even simpler, the reader may merely expand
$(1AA + 2Aa + 1aa)^4$ and then divide each term by $4^4 = 256$.
Further simplification can be achieved by replacing the double-
letter symbols (AA, Aa, aa) by some convenient single-letter
symbols, so the expression to be expanded will look something like
$(a + 2b + c)^4$. After multiplication and collecting terms with the
same number of the various genotypes, the reader can check his
results with those shown in Tables 1-2A and 1-2B. The expected

number of families in the table, divided by 256, gives the probability of the corresponding type of sibship. For example, the probability that the four children will be 1AA, 2Aa, 1aa (ignoring the order of birth) is 48/256 = .1875, or 18.75 per cent. The rest of the families do not show the ideal ratio. Among the 256 families there is a total of $4 \times 256 = 1,024$ children. It will be found from Table 1-2A that 256 of these children are AA, 512 are Aa, and 256 are aa. In other words, the Mendelian ratio (1:2:1) will be found in the total number of children of all the various types of sibship of Aa × Aa parents and *not* in any single small family.

TABLE 1-2A. TYPES OF SIBSHIPS OF FOUR CHILDREN FROM Aa × Aa PARENTS AND THEIR EXPECTED FREQUENCY IN 256 FAMILIES

Genotype of children	15 types of sibship															Total number of families
AA	4	3	3	2	2	2	1	**1**	1	1	0	0	0	0	0	
Aa	0	1	0	2	1	0	3	**2**	1	0	4	3	2	1	0	
aa	0	0	1	0	1	2	0	**1**	2	3	0	1	2	3	4	
Frequency	1	8	4	24	24	6	32	**48**	24	4	16	32	24	8	1	256

TABLE 1-2B. REARRANGEMENT OF TABLE 1-2A ACCORDING TO NUMBERS OF aa AND Aa*

	0 aa	1 aa	2 aa	3 aa	4 aa
4 Aa	16				
3 Aa	32	32			
2 Aa	24	**48**	24		
1 Aa	8	24	24	8	
0 Aa	1	4	6	4	1

* Since the number of children in each sibship is four, the number of AA children is implied. For example, the sibship with two aa and one Aa must have one AA.

If there is dominance, that is, if AA and Aa are of the same phenotype with a probability $\frac{1}{4} + \frac{1}{2} = \frac{3}{4}$, there will be only 5 (instead of 15) types of sibship. With the difference between

AA and Aa ignored, the expected frequencies of the 5 types of sibship in 256 families are the column sums of Table 1-2B, viz.,

Type of sibship: 0 aa   1 aa   2 aa   3 aa   4aa   Total
Expected number: 81   108   54   12   1   256

The array of the various types of sibship may, of course, be obtained directly by expanding $(\frac{3}{4} + \frac{1}{4})^4$. With dominance, the proportion of sibships that is expected to show the ideal 3:1 ratio is 108/256, or 42 per cent.

Examples and Applications

Haptoglobin is a plasma protein that combines specifically with hemoglobin. By the technique of starch-gel electrophoresis, persons can be classified on the basis of qualitative differences in the haptoglobins into three types designated as Hp 1-1, Hp 2-1, and Hp 2-2. Smithies and Walker (1955) showed that these three haptoglobin types are controlled by one pair of autosomal alleles. This genetic theory has been tested extensively in various parts of the world by many investigators, and the results have been found to conform with the family laws described in this chapter and with the population laws to be explained in the next chapter.

There are several other good examples of monofactorial inheritance in man. The M, MN, N blood typing is a very well-known one. A familiar example with dominance is the ability to taste phenylthiocarbamide. Those who can taste bitterness are TT and Tt, and the nontasters are tt.

In dealing with Mendelian inheritance in families there is only one fundamental principle to be remembered, and that is: one of the two genes of a given locus of any individual must have come from one parent and the other gene from the other parent. Thus, with regard to the individual Hp 2-1, one of his parents must have at least one Hp 2 gene, and the other parent must have at least one Hp 1 gene. Also, when the parents are Hp 1-1 × Hp 2-1, they cannot have an Hp 2-2 child. Furthermore, if a certain gene is absent in both parents, it cannot be present in their child.

As another example, persons suffering from sickle cell *anemia* are homozygous (say, SS), whereas those who have the sickle cell *trait* are heterozygous (AS). The original proof of this genetic hypothesis, given by Neel (1949), was the examination of 42 parents of 29 sickle cell anemia patients; every one of the parents had the sickle cell trait. The patient SS implies that each parent of his must have at least one S gene. Beet (1949) independently reached the same conclusion on the basis of extensive pedigrees.

These simple principles also constitute the foundation of the medicolegal applications of human genetics.

Sex Chromosomes and Sex-linked Genes

Now we come to the genes on the chromosome pair X,Y. Males and females all have 22 pairs of autosomes, but they differ in the X,Y pair. An individual with two X-chromosomes (denoted by XX) is a female; XY indicates a male. From the frontispiece we see that the X-chromosome is approximately five times as long as the Y-chromosome. This special pair is called the *sex chromosomes*.

Since a female is XX, all her eggs will contain an X; hence the female is called the *homogametic* sex. A male being XY, half his sperms will contain an X and half a Y; hence the male is called the *heterogametic* sex. When an X-sperm fertilizes an X-egg, the child will be a daughter, XX. When a Y-sperm fertilizes an X-egg, the child will be a son, XY. The average result is half girls and half boys:

$$\begin{array}{cccc} \text{Mother} & \text{Father} & \text{Daughter} & \text{Son} \\ \text{XX} & \times \quad \text{XY} & \rightarrow \ 50\% \ \text{XX} & + \ 50\% \ \text{XY} \end{array}$$

Since the egg is uniformly X-carrying and the sperms are of two types, it is the sperm that determines the sex of the child. The centuries-old tradition that a man (especially a king) may divorce his wife for not giving him a son, like so many other human traditions, is without justification. By the same token, the credit given to a queen in having a son is equally without justification. The whole problem has no more significance than having a head or a tail after tossing a coin.

The genes located on the X-chromosome are called *sex-linked genes*. At the present stage of our knowledge, Y does not seem to have any specific demonstrable genes, although it does play an important role in the development of a normal male. In the following, when we consider a single locus on X, we tacitly assume that Y has no counterpart and may be ignored. In other words, females (XX) are considered as diploids and males (XY) as haploids. For the A,a locus on X, there are three genotypes (AA, Aa, aa) among the females but only two genotypes (A·, a·) among the males, where the dot represents the Y-chromosome lacking the homologous locus. With respect to this single locus, there are $2 \times 3 = 6$ types of mating (Fig. 1-2). In each type,

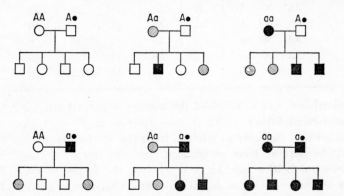

Fig. 1-2. The six types of families with respect to one pair of sex-linked genes. Plain, stippled, and solid circles are females of genotype AA, Aa, aa, respectively, whereas plain and solid squares are males of A• and a•, respectively; the dot stands for the Y-chromosome. There are no heterozygotes among males. In case of dominance, the stippled circles may be considered indistinguishable from the plain ones.

there are 50 per cent daughters and 50 per cent sons, but the proportions for the various genotypes within one sex differ. The detailed results are given in Table 1-3.

A pedigree involving a sex-linked locus, however complicated it is, can always be broken into the six basic types of family units illustrated in Fig. 1-2. In tracing a pedigree of sex-linked genes, there is only one extra rule to remember. The Y (or dot) of a father always goes to his son and the X always to his daughter, whatever the genotype.

A familiar example will help to grasp the characteristics of sex-linked inheritance. The common red-green color blindness is a sex-linked recessive trait, so AA and Aa women are normal, aa women are color-blind, A· men are normal, and a· men are

TABLE 1-3. FAMILY LAWS FOR SEX-LINKED GENES

Mother		Father	Daughters			Sons	
			AA	Aa	aa	A·	a·
AA	×	A·	.50	...	...	.50	
Aa	×	A·	.25	.25	...	.25	.25
aa	×	A·	...	.50	...	...	.50
AA	×	a·	...	.50	...	.50	
Aa	×	a·	...	.25	.25	.25	.25
aa	×	a·	...	...	.50	...	.50

color-blind. Let us consider the mating of normal mother AA × color-blind father a. Their sons receive the Y(dot) from the father and the normal allele A from the mother, so all the sons will be normal. Here we see that the "like father, like son" rule does not hold at all. In fact, whether the father is color-blind or not has nothing to do with his sons. Conversely, a color-blind son must have received his recessive gene from his mother; she must be either color-blind (aa) or a heterozygote ("carrier") Aa. It is through simple principles like these that a complicated pedigree is made understandable.

Hemophilia is another familiar sex-linked recessive trait. There are two major types of hemophilia; both are sex-linked recessive, or rather partially recessive. One of the purposes of the biochemical studies of hemophilia is to distinguish the heterozygous women (Aa) from the homozygous AA. A discussion of this subject is beyond the scope of this book.

Chapter 2

The Population Laws

In the preceding chapter we have studied the Mendelian ratios among the offspring of a given type of family with respect to one autosomal or sex-linked locus with two alleles. There may be hundreds, thousands, or millions of families in a human population. Throughout this chapter it is assumed that the population is very large. We may raise questions such as: What is the percentage of the three genotypes (AA, Aa, aa) in the general population? What is the relative frequency of each of the six types of families? To answer questions of this nature we need, in addition to the Mendelian law, two other specifications, which refer to the population as a whole. One is the mating system among individuals, and the other is gene frequency. The autosomal genes are considered first; the sex-linked genes are discussed briefly toward the end of this chapter.

Random Mating

Consider an arbitrary initial population in which 50 per cent of persons are AA, 20 per cent are Aa, and 30 per cent are aa. This population may be designated by (.50, .20, .30) for short. It is assumed that these genotypic proportions hold for both males and females. If men and women are married completely at random *with respect to this particular locus*, then the relative frequency of the six types of families is given by the appropriate terms of the product (.50 + .20 + .30)(.50 + .20 + .30). To facilitate the arithmetic, the product can be arranged into the form of a multiplication table, as shown at the top of page 16, but it is unnecessary for more experienced readers to do so.

15

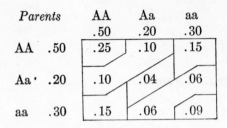

Parents		AA .50	Aa .20	aa .30
AA	.50	.25	.10	.15
Aa	.20	.10	.04	.06
aa	.30	.15	.06	.09

It is seen that among all the families in the population there are 25 per cent of the type AA × AA. This is also the probability that two random individuals will both be AA. When the relative frequencies of the mating types are determined by the (product) probability of independent events, we say that it is a system of *random mating*, or *panmixia*. It should be pointed out that the term *random mating* is a relative one. Here we mean that mating is random relative to the A, a locus under consideration such as the haptoglobin types, MN blood types, and so on. At the same time, mating may not be random with respect to height, education, intelligence, economic status, etc. The assumption of random mating with respect to certain genetic factors is no contradiction to assortative mating with respect to certain social factors or some other biological characteristics.

Counting AA × aa and aa × AA as the same type, as we did in the preceding chapter, we see that its total frequency is 15 + 15 = 30 per cent. Similarly, we pool the frequencies of other reciprocal crosses. The six types of families and their corresponding frequencies in the population are listed in the left half of Table 2-1. To calculate the offspring of these families, we apply the Mendelian laws to each type of family separately. Thus, for the 4 per cent Aa × Aa families in the population, ¼ of their offspring will be AA, ½Aa, and ¼aa. The offspring of the entire parental population are given in the right half of Table 2-1 in terms of relative frequencies. The next generation—the total offspring of all families—is seen to be (.36, .48, .16). The results obtained so far can be summarized by writing:

$$(.50, .20, .30) \rightarrow (.36, .48, .16)$$

The reader at this stage may not be able to see any necessary

TABLE 2-1. TYPES AND FREQUENCIES OF FAMILIES AND THEIR
OFFSPRING FOR AN ARBITRARY POPULATION (.50, .20, .30)
PRACTICING PANMIXIA

Parents		Offspring		
Type	Frequency	AA	Aa	aa
AA × AA	.25	.25	0	0
AA × Aa	.20	.10	.10	0
Aa × Aa	.04	.01	.02	.01
AA × aa	.30	0	.30	0
Aa × aa	.12	0	.06	.06
aa × aa	.09	0	0	.09
Total........	1.00	.36	.48	.16

relationship between the genotypic proportions of these two
generations. However, the relationship will become immediately
obvious when we consider another parameter of the population.

Gene Frequency

Although there are three genotypes in the population (.50,
.20, .30), there are only two kinds of genes, A and a; we may
ask: What proportion of the *genes* in the population is A and
what proportion is a? Now, the AA individuals have all A genes;
the Aa individuals have 50 per cent A genes and 50 per cent a
genes; the aa individuals have all a genes. Hence, the proportion
of genes in the population that are A and a are, respectively,

$$p = .50 + \tfrac{1}{2}(.20) = .60 \qquad q = \tfrac{1}{2}(.20) + .30 = .40$$

These are called *gene frequencies*. Thus, $p = .60$ is the frequency
of gene A, and $q = .40$ the frequency of gene a. Generally, in a
population (D, H, R) where $D + H + R = 1$, the gene frequencies are:

$$p = D + \tfrac{1}{2}H \qquad q = \tfrac{1}{2}H + R$$

These are, of course, also the frequencies of the A gametes and
a gametes produced by the genotypes of the population as a whole.

The random mating of individuals implies that any two gametes (from opposite sexes) are united at random. If there are $p = .60$ A gametes and $q = .40$ a gametes in the population, random union of these gametes will yield an offspring population with:

$$p^2 = .36 \text{ AA} \qquad 2pq = .48 \text{ Aa} \qquad q^2 = .16 \text{ aa}$$

as illustrated in Fig. 2-1. This explains the numerical results

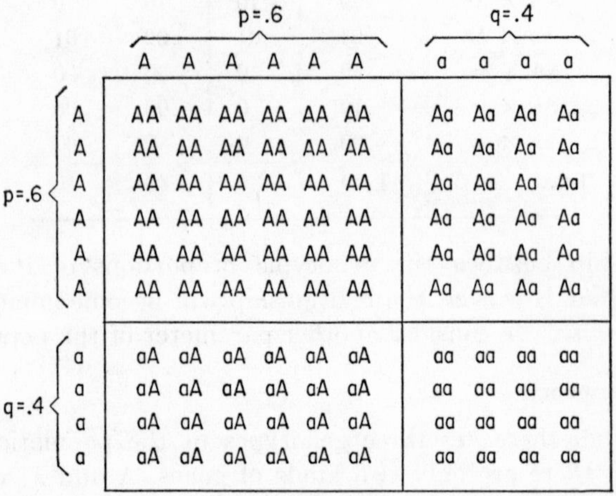

FIG. 2-1. The gene frequencies and equilibrium proportions of the three genotypes in a random-mating population.

obtained in the preceding section. It follows that the three initial genotypic proportions (.50, .20, .30) have no particular significance in a random-mating population except for their role in determining the gene frequencies $p = .60$ and $q = .40$. Any other initial population with the same gene frequency will yield the same offspring population on random mating. The reader may spend a few minutes to satisfy himself by showing that the initial population (.30, .60, .10) on random mating will yield the same (.36, .48, .16) offspring population.

An important principle is established in this section, viz., *the random mating of individuals is equivalent to the random union of gametes*. This principle will be employed many times in later chapters in dealing with more complicated situations in which a longhand enumeration of all the possible types of mating is very tedious.

Equilibrium Condition

The immediate next question is: What will be the composition of the offspring generation of the parental population

$$(p^2, 2pq, q^2) = (.36, .48, .16)$$

if random mating continues? Applying the principle just established above, we obtain the *gene* or *gamete frequencies:*

$$p = .36 + \tfrac{1}{2}(.48) = .60 \qquad q = \tfrac{1}{2}(.48) + .16 = .40$$

Random union of these gametes will yield an offspring population (.36, .48, .16) again. This shows that the population will remain the same in the absence of other disturbing factors. Such a population is said to be *in equilibrium.* This law was established independently by Hardy and Weinberg in the same year (1908) and hence is known as the Hardy-Weinberg law of equilibrium (see Stern, 1943).

Although the equilibrium has been established by a short cut, it is much more satisfying to demonstrate it by the long method, as shown in Table 2-2. In addition, we shall need all the details in the table for later discussions. This table is constructed exactly the same way as before, only replacing the arbitrary population by the one in equilibrium. For instance, the frequency of parental mating types is obtained from the terms of $(p^2AA + 2pqAa + q^2aa)^2 = (.36AA + .48Aa + .16aa)^2$. We see that the parental population $(p^2, 2pq, q^2)$ yields an offspring population of exactly the same composition.

Whatever the initial genotypic proportion, the equilibrium condition $(p^2, 2pq, q^2)$ *will be reached in one single generation of random mating and will remain so on continued random mating.* It is due to this simple theorem that we may safely take a human population to be in equilibrium with respect to one autosomal locus in practical research.

Comparing Table 2-2 in this section with Table 1-1 on family laws, we see that the chief difference is that in the present case there is the extra column for "frequency of mating." We may think of the frequency of mating as "weight" for the various types of families. Then, the total offspring of the six types of families, properly weighted, is $(p^2, 2pq, q^2)$.

TABLE 2-2. MATINGS AND OFFSPRING IN A LARGE RANDOM-MATING POPULATION WITH GENE FREQUENCIES $p = .60$ AND $q = .40$

Type of mating (mother × father)	Frequency of mating	Offspring		
		AA	Aa	aa
AA × AA	$p^4 = .1296$	$p^4 = .1296$	0	0
AA × Aa	$2p^3q = .1728$	$p^3q = .0864$	$p^3q = .0864$	0
AA × aa	$p^2q^2 = .0576$	0	$p^2q^2 = .0576$	0
Aa × AA	$2p^3q = .1728$	$p^3q = .0864$	$p^3q = .0864$	0
Aa × Aa	$4p^2q^2 = .2304$	$p^2q^2 = .0576$	$2p^2q^2 = .1152$	$p^2q^2 = .0576$
Aa × aa	$2pq^3 = .0768$	0	$pq^3 = .0384$	$pq^3 = .0384$
aa × AA	$p^2q^2 = .0576$	0	$p^2q^2 = .0576$	0
aa × Aa	$2pq^3 = .0768$	0	$pq^3 = .0384$	$pq^3 = .0384$
aa × aa	$q^4 = .0256$	0	0	$q^4 = .0256$
Reciprocals combined (Weinberg, 1908)				
AA × AA	$p^4 = .1296$	$p^4 = .1296$	0	0
AA × Aa	$4p^3q = .3456$	$2p^3q = .1728$	$2p^3q = .1728$	0
Aa × Aa	$4p^2q^2 = .2304$	$p^2q^2 = .0576$	$2p^2q^2 = .1152$	$p^2q^2 = .0576$
AA × aa	$2p^2q^2 = .1152$	0	$2p^2q^2 = .1152$	0
Aa × aa	$4pq^3 = .1536$	0	$2pq^3 = .0768$	$2pq^3 = .0768$
aa × aa	$q^4 = .0256$	0	0	$q^4 = .0256$
Total............	1.0000	$p^2 = .3600$	$2pq = .4800$	$q^2 = .1600$

Now let us consider the q^2, or the 16 per cent aa individuals in the general population. From the last column of Table 2-2, we see that they come from three types of families. The percentage from each type is as follows:

From Aa × Aa: $\dfrac{p^2q^2}{q^2} = \dfrac{.0576}{.1600} = 36\% = p^2$

From Aa × aa: $\dfrac{2pq^3}{q^2} = \dfrac{.0768}{.1600} = 48\% = 2pq$

From aa × aa: $\dfrac{q^4}{q^2} = \dfrac{.0256}{.1600} = 16\% = q^2$

Note that these percentages are identical with the genotypic proportions in the general population. Of course, this result may be seen directly (without referring to the table) by considering the probabilities. An aa individual implies that each parent has at least one a gene. These parents may thus be designated as Xa × Xa, where X is the undetermined gene. The probability that both Xs are A is p^2; that one is A and one is a is $2pq$; and that both are a is q^2.

Observational Verification

Before proceeding with the subject, let us look at some observed data to show that the Hardy-Weinberg law does actually hold in human populations.

The MN blood typing in man is a very familiar case in which all the three genotypes are distinguishable. Numerous published data from all parts of the world could be cited as examples; the following one has been chosen because it involves large numbers from a single community, and, as will be seen later, it also gives the frequency of the types of matings. Matsunaga and Itoh (1958) reported the following findings from the mining town

Genotype	Observed number	Gene frequency (estimate)	Expected proportion	Expected number
MM	406		.2756	408.44
		$p = .525$		
MN	744		.4988	739.22
		$q = .475$		
NN	332		.2256	334.34
Total....	$G = 1,482$	1.000	1.0000	1,482.00

Ashibetsu in Hokkaido, Japan: When all three genotypes are distinguishable, a sample of $G = 1,482$ persons from a random-mating population is equivalent to a sample of $2G = 2,964$ genes. Each of 406 MM individuals, traditionally referred to as M individuals, has two M genes, whereas each of the 744 MN individuals has one M gene. Hence, there are $2(406) + 744 = 1,556$ M genes among a total of 2,964. The frequency of the M gene is then $1,556/2,964 = .525 = p$, and that of the N gene is

$$1 - .525 = .475 = q$$

This is not the true (but unknown) gene frequency of the Ashibetsu population but the estimate of it based on the observed sample. In statistical literature the sample estimate is written as $\hat{p}$ or some other symbol to be distinguished from the true value (parameter). We shall not go too much into the sampling theory, and it is not necessary to use a new symbol. It is always understood that anything calculated from the sample is a sample estimate and is subject to sampling error.

The expected proportions of the three genotypes are the terms of $(p + q)^2 = (.525 + .475)^2$ in accordance with the Hardy-Weinberg law. Multiplying these expected proportions by $G = 1,482$, we obtain the expected numbers. It is seen that these expected numbers agree very well with those observed. The "goodness of fit" may be tested by the usual chi-square method. The value of χ^2 in this sample is 0.06 with one degree of freedom, showing a very insignificant deviation (that is, good fit) between the observed and expected numbers.

The sampling estimate ($p = .525$ for this particular sample) varies from sample to sample. If another sample were taken from Ashibetsu, the p value would be somewhat different from .525. The sampling variance of p or q is:

$$V(p) = V(q) = \frac{pq}{2G} = \frac{.525 \times .475}{2(1,482)} = .000084$$

and the standard error of p or q is the square root of the variance:

$$s(p) = s(q) = \sqrt{.000084} = .0092$$

The 1,482 persons above actually consist of 741 couples. The six mating types and their numbers are as follows:

Mating type	Observed number	Expected proportion	Expected number
MM × MM	58	$p^4 = .0760$	56.3
MM × MN	202	$4p^3q = .2749$	203.7
MN × MN	190	$4p^2q^2 = .2487$	184.3
MM × NN	88	$2p^2q^2 = .1244$	92.2
MN × NN	162	$4pq^3 = .2251$	166.8
NN × NN	41	$q^4 = .0509$	37.7
Total..........	741	1.00	741.0

In calculating the expected proportions for the various types of mating, the value $p = .525$ is employed. The expected and observed number of the mating types agree very well, and there is little doubt that the population is panmictic with respect to the genetic factors M, N. This furnishes us an observational proof of the general validity of the assumption of random mating and equilibrium.

Sex-linked Genes

The original Hardy-Weinberg law for a large random-mating population is established for autosomal genes only, but it also applies with slight modification to sex-linked genes *when the population is in equilibrium state.* The equilibrium state occurs when among females the genotypic proportions are p^2, $2pq$, q^2 as in the autosomal situation and among the males the proportions are simply p, q. This is demonstrated in Table 2-3, in which, for the sake of omitting the constant factor ½, the daughters and sons are listed as two separate populations of offspring; in each population the proportions add up to unity.

Several observations may be made on the equilibrium condition. Each female has two X-chromosomes, and each male has only one. If there are equal numbers of both sexes in the population, then ⅔ of the sex-linked genes are in the female population and ⅓ in the male population. However, the gene frequencies in the two sexes are equal, both being p and q. This is an essential condition for equilibrium.

The proportion of males that possesses a sex-linked trait is always greater than the proportion of females that is homozygous for the locus. For instance, if $q = \frac{1}{12} = 8.33$ per cent of the

TABLE 2-3. EQUILIBRIUM CONDITION FOR SEX-LINKED GENES IN A
LARGE RANDOM-MATING POPULATION

Mother		Father	Frequency of mating	Daughters			Sons	
				AA	Aa	aa	A·	a·
AA	×	A·	p^3	p^3	...	...	p^3	
Aa	×	A·	$2p^2q$	p^2q	p^2q	...	p^2q	p^2q
aa	×	A·	pq^2	...	pq^2	...	...	pq^2
AA	×	a·	p^2q	...	p^2q	...	p^2q	
Aa	×	a·	$2pq^2$	...	pq^2	pq^2	pq^2	pq^2
aa	×	a·	q^3	...	...	q^3	...	q^3
Total.............			1.00	p^2	$2pq$	q^2	p	q

males are color-blind, then the proportion of color-blind females is only $q^2 = \frac{1}{144} = 0.69$ per cent, less than $\frac{7}{10}$ of 1 per cent. This explains why there are so few color-blind females in comparison with males. The smaller the value of q, the greater the departure between female and male proportions. Hemophilia is much rarer than color blindness, so hemophiliac females must be very rare indeed. In addition to the q and q^2 relationship, there might be other factors affecting the incidence of female hemophiliacs. So far, only a paucity of cases has been reported.

The Approach to Equilibrium

With respect to an autosomal locus, equilibrium condition is reached in one generation of random mating. Because of the asymmetry in the two sexes, equilibrium is in general not reached in one generation of random mating for a sex-linked locus, except in special cases, but is approached very rapidly in successive generations of random mating. The details have been given elsewhere (Li, 1955a), and only a brief mention of the main features of the converging process is given here.

Suppose that among female parents the gene frequency is $q_{xx} = .32$ and that among male parents $q_x = .56$. The genotype of the sons is entirely determined by that of mothers and has nothing to do with the fathers. Hence the gene frequency among the sons will be the same (i.e., .32) as that among the mothers. A daughter's genotype is determined half by the mother and half by the father; therefore the gene frequency among the daughters is the average of their parental gene frequencies, that is, $\frac{1}{2}(.32 + .56) = .44$. Continuing this process, we obtain the following results:

Generation t	Females q_{xx}	Males q_x	Difference $q_{xx} - q_x$	Pooled frequency $\bar{q} = (2q_{xx} + q_x)/3$
0	.32	.56	−.24	.40
1	.44	.32	+.12	.40
2	.38	.44	−.06	.40
3	.41	.38	+.03	.40
...	.40	.40	0	.40

We see that each male gene frequency is equal to the female gene frequency of the previous generation and each female gene frequency is the average of two parental gene frequencies. The absolute difference between the female and male gene frequencies is halved in each generation. The shuffling of genes from one sex to another does not change the average or pooled gene frequency of the two sexes, as shown in the last column. In the equilibrium state, the gene frequency is equal to $\bar{q}$ in both sexes. In practice, it is safe to take a human population as in equilibrium, except in a newly intermixed race.

APPENDIX ON ALGEBRAIC SIMPLIFICATIONS

Those who have no occasion to use algebra tend to forget the elementary manipulations they learned many years ago. This appendix serves to review some of the relations encountered frequently in the rest of the book, so that they need not block the reader when he sees them. One identity that the reader must be familiar with is:

$$(a + b)(a - b) = a^2 - b^2$$

This we shall use very often.

First, consider the linear expressions. If p and q are two positive fractions and $p + q = 1$, we may draw a straight line of unit length and divide it into two parts, one of length p and the other of length q, so a linear expression can always be thought of as a length.

$$p = 1 - q \qquad q = 1 - p$$
$$p + 2q = 1 + q = 2 - p \quad 3 + q = 4 - p,$$
$$p - q = 1 - 2q = -2(q - \tfrac{1}{2})$$

Next, consider expressions involving the second power. Many of the following expressions may be seen by drawing a *unit square* with each side divided into p and q, so the unit area is $1 = p^2 + 2pq + q^2$. Thus $(p + q) \times q = 1 \times q = q$ stands for the *area* of a rectangle of unit length and q width.

$$pq = q(1 - q) = p(1 - p) = q - q^2 = p - p^2$$
$$p^2 + pq = p(p + q) = p \quad \text{similarly,} \quad q^2 + pq = q$$
$$p^2 + 2pq = 1 - q^2 \quad = (1 - q)(1 + q) = p(p + 2q)$$
$$\qquad\qquad\qquad = p(2 - p) \qquad = p(1 + q) = p + pq$$
$$p^2 - q^2 = (p + q)(p - q) = p - q = 1 - 2q$$

In certain types of problems we encounter expressions involving the third power:

$$p^3 + p^2q = p^2(p + q) = p^2$$
$$p^2q + pq^2 = pq(p + q) = pq$$

In dealing with mating types, expressions involving the fourth power come up very often. Usually there is more than one way of simplifying such expressions.

$$p^2q^2 + 2pq^3 + q^4 = q^2(p^2 + 2pq + q^2) \quad = q^2$$
$$p^4 + 4p^3q + 4p^2q^2 = (p^2 + 2pq)^2 \qquad\quad = (1 - q^2)^2$$
$$= p^2(p^2 + 4pq + 4q^2) = p^2(p + 2q)^2$$
$$= p^2(1 + q)^2$$
$$q^4 + pq^3 + \tfrac{1}{4}p^2q^2 = \tfrac{1}{4}q^2(1 + q)^2$$

Finally, expressions may involve quantities other than p and q. In the following, s is a positive fraction.

$$q(1 - s) - q(1 - sq) = -spq$$
$$p^2 + 2pq(1 - s) + q^2(1 - s)^2 = (1 - sq)^2$$
$$pq(1 - s) + q^2(1 - s)^2 = q(1 - s)(1 - sq)$$

These few examples must suffice. After a certain amount of practice, the reader should be able to simplify similar expressions without difficulty. The meaning of an expression often gives a hint as to how it should be simplified.

Chapter 3

Study of Population and Families

A numerical example was given in Chap. 2, using the MN data to show that both mating frequencies and genotypic proportions are in close agreement with the Hardy-Weinberg law. This chapter gives some examples not so simple as that of the MN system. The most common complication arises from dominance such that the heterozygous proportion cannot be directly observed. Previously, p and q have been used to denote the gene frequencies in a population (parameters). When a random sample of individuals is taken from a population, the values of the true but unknown parameters can only be estimated from the sample and these estimates are subject to random-sampling error. In formal writing, the sample estimate of the true q is denoted by $\hat{q}$, q', or some other notation. In the following, however, we shall drop any notation for simplicity, and the context will make it clear whether we are talking about the estimate or the parameter.

Expected Number of Genotypes

Let us consider the sample observed by Sutton et al. (1959) with respect to the haptoglobin types of American white persons:

Haptoglobin type:	(1-1)	(1-2)	(2-2)	Total
Observed number:	$a = 9$	$b = 40$	$c = 19$	$G = 68$

The theoretical proportion for the heterozygotes is $2pq$, whose numerical value cannot exceed .500. The observed proportion of heterozygotes is $40/68 = .588$. The observed excess is, however, not statistically significant on account of the small numbers.

The estimate of gene frequency is:

$$p_1 = \frac{2a + b}{2G} = \frac{58}{136} = .42647 \qquad p_2 = \frac{b + 2c}{2G} = \frac{78}{136} = .57353$$

where p_1 and p_2 have the same meaning as our previous p and q but are more natural in this example. The variance of such estimates is $p_1 p_2 / 2G$, as described in the last chapter. The expected numbers of the three genotypes are $G(p_1 + p_2)^2$, and a chi-square test can be made to ascertain the "goodness of fit" with the observed numbers.

For small samples of this type, there is a more exact method of calculating the expected number of genotypes. For brevity, we let the number of Hp 1 and Hp 2 alleles in the sample be $g_1 = 2a + b$, and $g_2 = b + 2c$, respectively. With these numbers also fixed, the expected numbers of the three genotypes in a sample of G individuals (Levene, 1949) are:

Hp 1-1	Hp 1-2	Hp 2-2
$\dfrac{g_1(g_1 - 1)}{2(2G - 1)}$	$\dfrac{g_1 g_2}{2G - 1}$	$\dfrac{g_2(g_2 - 1)}{2(2G - 1)}$

The expected numbers based on this formula and those based on Gp_1^2, etc., for our example are as follows:

	(1-1)	(1-2)	(2-2)	chi square, 1 d.f.
Expected(p_1, p_2):	12.37	33.26	22.37	$\chi^2 = 2.79$
Expected(g_1, g_2):	12.24	33.51	22.24	$\chi^2 = 2.59$

Note that expected number of homozygotes based on the $g_1 g_2$ formula is always smaller than those calculated on the $p_1 p_2$ method. The improvement in fitness is negligible in this example. When one of the alleles has a very low frequency or several small samples are combined, the exact formula may be quite useful.

Estimate of Recessive Gene Frequencies

When AA and Aa are of the same phenotype, the population will consist of $p^2 + 2pq = 1 - q^2$ dominants and q^2 recessives. With only two phenotypes in the population, the method of estimating the gene frequency is different from that used for the

MN system and the estimate is less accurate. For example, in an observed sample of $G = 1,600$ random individuals, 1,139 of them are found to be able to taste phenylthiocarbamide (tasters, dominant) and $R = 461$ are nontasters (recessive). The proportion of recessives, $R/G = 461/1,600 = .288$, is an estimate of q^2. Hence the value of q is estimated by:

$$q = \sqrt{\frac{R}{G}} = \sqrt{\frac{461}{1,600}} = \sqrt{.288} = .537$$

and $p = 1 - q = .463$. The sampling variance of such an estimate is:

$$V(q) = \frac{1 - q^2}{4G} = \frac{1 - .288}{4(1,600)} = .000111$$
$$= \frac{pq}{2G} + \frac{p^2}{4G}$$

The standard error is $s(q) = \sqrt{.000111} \doteq 0.010$. The last expression for $V(q)$ is not for practical calculation but is intended to emphasize the fact that the variance is larger than $pq/2G$. When there is dominance, the number of a genes hidden in the heterozygotes is unknown and the estimate is based on the porportion of recessive individuals only. The more dominant genes there are in the population, the less accurate is the estimate and the larger the component $p^2/4G$.

For small samples, although R/G is an unbiased estimate of q^2, $\sqrt{R/G}$ is a *biased* estimate of q. This means that the average value of $\sqrt{R/G}$ from all possible samples of size G is not quite equal to the true q of the population. Haldane (1956) suggests that:

$$\sqrt{\frac{R + \frac{1}{4}}{G + \frac{1}{4}}} = \sqrt{\frac{4R + 1}{4G + 1}}$$

is a better estimate of q. The variance of such an estimate is approximately $(1 - q^2)/(4G + 1)$. Table 3-1 shows how this estimate compares with the traditional $\sqrt{R/G}$ for a very small sample. It is assumed that in the population the true value of q is .7071, so the probability that an individual is recessive is $q^2 = .50$. The sampling distribution of the number of recessive individuals in a sample of 5 is $(\frac{1}{2} + \frac{1}{2})^5$. We see that the average value of the improved estimate is .705, being closer to the true value than the average traditional estimate .68.

TABLE 3-1. COMPARISON OF TWO ESTIMATES OF RECESSIVE GENE FREQUENCY IN SAMPLES OF $G = 5$ INDIVIDUALS FROM A POPULATION IN WHICH $q^2 = \frac{1}{2}$ AND $q = .7071$

Observed number of recessives R	Number of samples	$\sqrt{\dfrac{R}{G}}$	$\sqrt{\dfrac{R + \frac{1}{4}}{G + \frac{1}{4}}}$
0	1	0	.2182
1	5	.4472	.4880
2	10	.6325	.6547
3	10	.7746	.7868
4	5	.8944	.8997
5	1	1.0000	1.0000
Total or mean....	32	.6806	.7054

Population Ratios

When there is dominance, not all the six types of mating listed in the lower half of Table 2-2 are distinguishable. The first three types of mating are phenotypically the same and may be pooled into one type designated as *dominant × dominant*. Similarly, the fourth and fifth types of mating involve one dominant and one recessive parent and may be pooled together as *dominant × recessive*. In the offspring columns, AA and Aa are likewise pooled into one dominant group. The result of such pooling is shown in Table 3-2.

For each of the six types of families in Table 2-2, the proportion of recessive offspring is 0, or $\frac{1}{4}$, or $\frac{1}{2}$, or 1, determined by Mendelian law. This, however, is not the case with dominance, because the so-called dominant × dominant families constitute a mixture of three types of genotypic matings and the dominant × recessive families a mixture of two. Only the recessive × recessive families remain the same as before, yielding 100 per cent recessive offspring. The proportion of recessive offspring among

TABLE 3-2. TYPES OF MATING AND OFFSPRING IN A PANMICTIC POPULATION WHEN THERE IS DOMINANCE (CONDENSED FROM TABLE 2-2)

Type of mating	Frequency of mating	Offspring		Proportion of recessive offspring
		Dominant	Recessive	
dom × dom	$(1 - q^2)^2 = .7056$	$p^2(1 + 2q) = .6480$	$p^2q^2 = .0576$	$S_2 = \dfrac{.0576}{.7056} = \dfrac{4}{49} = .0816$
dom × rec	$2q^2(1 - q^2) = .2688$	$2pq^2 = .1920$	$2pq^3 = .0768$	$S_1 = \dfrac{.0768}{.2688} = \dfrac{2}{7} = .2857$
rec × rec	$q^4 = .0256$	0	$q^4 = .0256$	$S_0 = \dfrac{.0256}{.0256} = 1.0000$
Total.........	1.0000	$1 - q^2 = .8400$	$q^2 = .1600$	

the children of the dominant $\times$ recessive parents is, from Table 3-2,

$$S_1 = \frac{2pq^3}{2q^2(1 - q^2)} = \frac{q}{1 + q} = \frac{.40}{1.40} = \frac{2}{7}$$

That the S_1 is the weighted average recessive proportion for two types of families may be seen more clearly from Table 2-2. There are $2p^2q^2$ AA $\times$ aa families that produce no recessive offspring, and there are $4pq^3$ Aa $\times$ aa families that produce 50 per cent recessive offspring. Hence, the weighted proportion of recessive offspring for these two types of families is

$$S_1 = \frac{2p^2q^2(0) + 4pq^3(\frac{1}{2})}{2p^2q^2 + 4pq^3} = \frac{2pq^3}{2pq^2(p + 2q)} = \frac{q}{1 + q}$$

$$= \frac{0 + .0768}{.1152 + .1536} = \frac{.0768}{.2688} = \frac{2}{7}$$

Being a weighted average of 0 and $\frac{1}{2}$, the value of $S_1 = q/(1 + q)$ is always between 0 and $\frac{1}{2}$. The formula for S_1 may also be derived from other considerations, but we need not go into all the details.

Similarly, the proportion of recessives among the offspring of dominant $\times$ dominant parents is the weighted average proportion for the three genotypic matings which produce 0, 0, $\frac{1}{4}$ recessives. The average proportion is

$$S_2 = \frac{p^2q^2}{p^2(1 + q)^2} = \frac{q^2}{(1 + q)^2} = S_1^2$$

$$= \frac{.0576}{.7056} = \frac{4}{49} = \left(\frac{2}{7}\right)^2$$

The value of S_2 is always smaller than $\frac{1}{4}$, ignoring the trivial cases $q = 0$ or 1.

Although the Mendelian ratios are constants for each type of family, the weighted average proportion for a mixture of several types of families is a function of gene frequency, because the weights (frequencies) of the various types of families are determined by gene frequencies. S_1 and S_2 are called *population ratios* by Snyder (1934). They vary from trait to trait in the same population, depending on the frequency of the gene determining the trait under consideration; they also vary from population to population for the same trait, depending on the frequency of the gene in the respective populations.

Let us close this section with a well-known example. In Table 3-3 are given the offspring of 800 families classified accord-

TABLE 3-3. INHERITANCE OF THE ABILITY TO TASTE PHENYLTHIOCAR-BAMIDE (PTC) IN MAN AND POPULATION RATIOS (SNYDER, 1932)

| Parental type | Number | Number of Children | | | Nontaster Proportion | |
		Taster	Nontaster	Total	Observed	Calculated
Taster × taster	425	929	130	1,059	$S_2 = .123$	$S_2 = .122$
Taster × nontaster	289	483	278	761	$S_1 = .365$	$S_1 = .349$
Nontaster × nontaster	86	5*	218	223	$S_0 = .978*$	$S_3 = 1.000$
Total...............	800	1,417	626	2,043		

* May be due to illegitimacies, adoptions, errors in diagnosis, etc. See section on Proportion of Illegitimacy.

ing to the phenotypes of the parents. Of the 1,600 parents, $2(86) + 289 = 461$ are nontasters (recessives), so

$$q = \sqrt{461/1{,}600} = \sqrt{.288} = .537$$

as obtained before. A better estimate of the gene frequency could be made based on both parents and children, but we shall not go into that subject. The expected values of the population ratios are $S_1 = q/(1 + q) = .537/1.537 = .349$ and

$$S_2 = (.349)^2 = .122$$

These are in close agreement with those observed:

$$S_1' = {}^{278}\!/_{761} = .365$$

and $S_2' = 130/1{,}059 = .123$. The sampling variance of S_1 and S_2 are:

$$V(S_1) = \frac{1 - q^2}{4G(1 + q)^4} \qquad V(S_2) = \frac{q^2(1 - q^2)}{G(1 + q)^6}$$

where G is the number of independent persons (1,600 in example) used to estimate the gene frequency.

Proportion of Illegitimacy

The five taster (dominant) children from nontaster × nontaster parents shown in Table 3-3 could be due to a variety of reasons, such as illegitimacies, adoptions, and wrong diagnosis. In this section we shall assume that they are all illegitimate children and estimate the proportion of illegitimacy. This is probably an overestimate; our main concern here is the methodology.

At first glance, there seems only $5/223 = 2.24$ per cent illegitimacy, but this is not true; for should the illegitimate child be a nontaster, he would not be directly detected. The five observed are only the dominant illegitimacies. Let i be the proportion of illegitimacy, and we assume that the father involved is a random individual (genotypewise) and could be AA, Aa, aa with probabilities p^2, $2pq$, q^2. Then the probability that the contribution from the father is A is p. The situation would be as follows:

Mother	Father	Frequency	Taster children	Nontaster children
aa	aa	$1 - i$	0	$1 - i$
aa	Random	i	ip	iq
Total.......		1.00	ip	$1 - ip$

Hence we obtain the equation $ip = 5/223$. If $p = .463$ in this population,

$$i = \frac{5}{223 \times .463} = 4.84\%$$

Although this estimate is reached on the basis of recessive families, it is reasonable to assume that the same proportion applies to all types of matings; that is, illegitimacy is independent of the ability to taste phenylthiocarbamide.

Multiple Recessiveness

The method of population ratio described under Population Ratios, in fact, only establishes the recessiveness of the trait (inability to taste PTC) and does not in itself imply that the trait is monofactorial. Suppose that the ability to taste PTC is determined by two "duplicate" loci, so a taster has at least one A gene *or* one B gene and only the genotype aabb is a nontaster. The population still consists of only two phenotypes of individuals and three types of mating. If we let p be the joint frequency of AB, Ab, and aB gametes, and q be that of ab gametes, it may be shown (Li, 1953b) that the property of inheritance is identical with that described in Table 3-2. The segregation behavior

$$S_0 = 1 \qquad S_1 = \frac{q}{1+q} \qquad S_2 = S_1^2$$

may be termed the general population ratio for recessive inheritance, whether the recessive trait is due to one, two, or more duplicate loci.

Relatives and Identical Genes

There are many types of relatives in a human community. In this chapter only the most common and very close relatives, viz., immediate family members, will be considered, with brief mention of some other types of relatives. As we shall see later, the genetic relationship falls rapidly with remote relatives. In the author's opinion, it would be better and more economical in most cases to study a large number of family units (parents and children) than to spend time and efforts in tracing first and second cousins. The only other type of relative we shall consider in any detail later in this book is first cousins in connection with inbreeding (Chap. 10).

To clarify the concept of the identity of a gene, let X denote an allele of the A,a locus. It may be A or a. We are now not considering the phase or state of the allele, but its identity. With the X notation, parents and their children can then be represented as follows:

$$\text{Mother:} \quad X_1X_2 \qquad \text{Father:} \; X_3X_4$$
$$\text{Children:} \quad X_1X_3, \; X_1X_4, \; X_2X_3, \; X_2X_4$$

where the subscripts 1, 2, 3, 4 are labels to identify the particular gene, whatever phase (A or a) it may be. It is seen that each child has one and only one gene in common with any one parent. For instance, the child X_1X_3 has X_1 in common with the mother. No child can have both genes in common with either parent. From this point of view, the parent-child relationship may be thought of as two individuals having one gene in common. The X_1 of mother X_1X_2 and the X_1 of child X_1X_3 are the same genes, the latter being derived from the former. These two genes are said to be *identical by descent*. Identical genes are necessarily of the same phase; that is, if X_1 of mother is A, then the X_1 of child is necessarily A, barring mutation. It is also clear that a parent-child pair has only three independent genes, the fourth being identical with one of the parent's.

Now let us consider the relationship among the children (brothers and sisters). The four types shown above are equally likely, each with a probability $\frac{1}{4}$. If both brothers are of the type X_1X_3 (or both X_1X_4, or both X_2X_3, or both X_2X_4), these two brothers have both genes in common. The total probability for this event is $\frac{1}{4}$. When two brothers have both genes in common, they will be of the same genotype (whether it is AA, Aa, or aa). On the other hand, two brothers may not have any gene in common at all, such as the sib pair X_1X_3 and X_2X_4, or the pair X_1X_4 and X_2X_3. In such an event, which also has a probability of $\frac{1}{4}$, the two brothers are no different from two unrelated persons, as far as this locus is concerned. Finally, two brothers may have one gene in common (e.g., X_1X_3 and X_2X_3) with a probability of $\frac{1}{2}$. In this case, the two brothers are related in the same way as a parent is to his child.

Relatives are persons who are connected in such a way that they may have identical genes in common. In order to have identical genes in common, they must share at least one common ancestor. Ordinarily, husband and wife are not relatives, still less the in-laws. It is puzzling to see that certain in-laws are included as relatives of patients in some recent studies of heredity of breast and uterine cancer.

Conditional Probability

From the viewpoint of the identity of a gene, relatives can be classified into three kinds: those with both genes in common.

those with one gene in common, and those with no gene in common. When the genotype of one member of a pair of relatives is known (given or fixed), the conditional probability for the genotype of the other member is easily calculated. The probabilities are given in Table 3-4.

TABLE 3-4. CONDITIONAL PROBABILITY FOR THE GENOTYPE OF A
RELATIVE WHEN THE GENOTYPE OF THE OTHER RELATIVE
IS GIVEN

Given	Both genes in common (e.g., identical twins)			One gene in common (e.g., parent-child)			No gene in common (unrelated individuals)		
	AA	Aa	aa	AA	Aa	aa	AA	Aa	aa
AA		1	0	0	p	q	0	p^2	$2pq$	q^2
Aa	$I =$	0	1	0	$\frac{1}{2}p$	$\frac{1}{2}$	$\frac{1}{2}q$	p^2	$2pq$	q^2
aa		0	0	1	0	p	q	p^2	$2pq$	q^2

(with $T =$ preceding the One gene in common matrix and $O =$ preceding the No gene in common matrix)

Suppose that one relative is known to be Aa; what is the probability that the other relative is AA if they have one gene in common? The common gene between them must be A, and the probability of its being transmitted is $\frac{1}{2}$. The probability that the other (random) gene is A is p, so the probability that the other relative is AA is $\frac{1}{2}p$, as shown in the second row of T. The probabilities in the I and O matrices are obvious and need no explanation.

The probabilities given in Table 3-4 are very fundamental for many problems in random-mating populations. The use of these probabilities can often reduce a long and tedious algebraic process to a simple operation of addition. Some of the applications have been given by Li and Sacks (1954), and we shall use them here only for the limited purpose of obtaining probabilities of parent-child pairs and sib-sib pairs in a human population.

Mother-Child Combinations

When the mother's genotype is given, the conditional probabilities for the child's genotype are the elements of T in Table 3-4. Multiplying the first row by p^2, the second row by $2pq$, and the third by q^2, we obtain the probability (or relative frequency) of the various mother-child pairs (Table 3-5) in the population. The reader, to convince himself that this short cut is correct, may go back to Table 2-2 and combine the three matings involving the same genotype of mother and offspring and see that the answers so obtained are identical with those given in Table 3-5. It is of practical value to know the expected frequencies of mother-child pairs because some types of mild incompatibility studies are based on this knowledge.

TABLE 3-5. FREQUENCY OF MOTHER-CHILD COMBINATIONS

	Without dominance				*With dominance*		
	Child				*Child*		
	AA	Aa	aa	Total	dom	rec	Total
AA	p^3	p^2q	0	p^2			
Mother Aa	p^2q	pq	pq^2	$2pq$	$1 - 2q^2 + q^3$	pq^2	$1 - q^2$
aa	0	pq^2	q^3	q^2	pq^2	q^3	q^2
Total	p^2	$2pq$	q^2	1.00	$1 - q^2$	q^2	1.00

	Numerical example				*Numerical example*		
	M	MN	N	Total	Rh+	Rh−	Total
M	$a_1 = 93$	$a_2 = 74$	0	167			
MN	$a_3 = 69$	$a_4 = 151$	$a_5 = 60$	280	+ $a = 45$	$b = 12$	57
N	0	$a_6 = 59$	$a_7 = 50$	109	− $c = 14$	$d = 9$	23
Total	162	284	110	$556=G$	59	21	$80 = G$

When there is no dominance, the gene frequency may be easily estimated from the observed data. In the lower part of Table 3-5, a_1 is the observed number of mother M–child M *pairs*, and G is the total number of mother-child *pairs*. Conventionally, m and n (in lieu of p and q) are used to denote the frequency of the M and N gene, and the phenotype M is of genotype MM and, similarly, N of NN. The following estimate of the gene frequency is fully efficient:

$$m = \frac{3a_1 + 2(a_2 + a_3) + a_4 + a_5 + a_6}{3G - a_4} = \frac{835}{1,517} = 0.55043$$

Note that the numerical multiplier of the observed a's in the numerator is the power of p in the corresponding theoretical frequency table. The variance and standard error of the estimate is:

$$V(m) = \frac{mn}{3G - a_4} = .0001631 \qquad s(m) = .01277$$

When there is dominance, however, the fully efficient method of estimating the recessive gene frequency or the proportion of recessive individuals based on the observed number of mother-child pairs is complicated (Fisher, 1940), and can hardly be presented here. To estimate the proportion of recessive individuals, we shall simply count the total number of recessives in the sample and use the following estimate, based on the observed numbers of Rh pairs:

$$q^2 = \frac{12 + 14 + 2(9)}{2 \times 80} = \frac{44}{160} = 27.50\%$$

Since each mother-child pair has only three independent genes and, in other words, is equivalent to 1.50 unrelated persons, the variance of q^2 as estimated above may be taken approximately:

$$V(q^2) = \frac{.275 \times .725}{80 \times 1.50} = \frac{.1994}{120} = .001661 \quad \text{s.d.} = 4.08\%$$

By a more exact method of scores and weights, Fisher's (1940) estimate of q^2 is 27.44 per cent (versus our 27.50); his denominator is 119.14 (versus our 120), and the standard error is 4.09 per cent (versus our 4.08). It is seen that, while the crude method is not fully efficient, it will not distort the result to any appreciable extent.

Full Sib-Sib Combinations

It has been pointed out under Relatives and Identical Genes that $\frac{1}{4}$ of the time two brothers have both genes in common,

$\frac{1}{2}$ of the time they have one gene in common, and $\frac{1}{4}$ of the time they have no gene in common. Hence the conditional probability for the genotype of one brother when that of the other is given is:

$$S = \frac{1}{4}I + \frac{1}{2}T + \frac{1}{4}O$$

where I, T, O are the matrices in Table 3-4. For example, when one brother is given to be AA, the conditional probability for the other brother to be also AA is:

$$\frac{1}{4}(1) + \frac{1}{2}(p) + \frac{1}{4}(p^2) = \frac{1}{4}(1 + p)^2$$

The probability for all other combinations is calculated in the same way. After all nine such probabilities are calculated, multiply the first row by p^2, the second row by $2pq$, and the third row by q^2. The result is the joint distribution of full sib pairs (Table 3-6). Again, the reader, if he wishes, can go back to Table 2-2 and calculate the frequencies of the various combinations of sib pairs produced by each type of mating and then add the contributions from all six matings together. The result, if there are no mistakes in algebra, should be identical with that of Table 3-6.

Schiff and Verschuer (1933) studied 244 pairs of dizygotic twins with respect to ABO and MN blood types. Because dizygotic twins are genetically like ordinary brothers and sisters except that they are born at the same time (i.e., a litter of size two), the frequencies of the various twin combinations with respect to MN should be the same as those for ordinary siblings. It is to verify this point that the MN twin data are also cited in Table 3-6. If the distinction between the first and the second twin in the original data is ignored, there will be only six types of twin pairs (or sib pairs), as shown at the bottom of the table.

Again, the exact estimation of gene frequency from sib-pair data is difficult. A crude counting of the number of M (i.e., A) genes will suffice for our purpose. Each of the 45 M-M pairs has four M genes, etc. The proportion of the M genes is then (using m for p):

$$m = \frac{4(45) + 3(53) + 2(78 + 3) + 36}{4(244)} = \frac{537}{976} = 0.55$$

TABLE 3-6. FREQUENCIES OF FULL SIB PAIRS

	AA	Aa	aa	Total
AA	$\frac{1}{4}p^2(1+p)^2$	$\frac{1}{2}p^2q(1+p)$	$\frac{1}{4}p^2q^2$	p^2
Aa	$\frac{1}{2}p^2q(1+p)$	$pq(1+pq)$	$\frac{1}{2}pq^2(1+q)$	$2pq$
aa	$\frac{1}{4}p^2q^2$	$\frac{1}{2}pq^2(1+q)$	$\frac{1}{4}q^2(1+q)^2$	q^2
Total	p^2	$2pq$	q^2	1.00

Numerical example (Schiff and Verschuer, 1933)

	M	MN	N	
M	45	20	3	68
MN	33	78	14	125
N	0	22	29	51
Total	78	120	46	244

Reciprocal pairs combined

Pair type	AA AA	AA Aa	Aa Aa	AA aa	Aa aa	aa aa	Total
Freq.	$\frac{1}{4}p^2(1+p)^2$	$p^2q(1+p)$	$pq(1+pq)$	$\frac{1}{2}p^2q^2$	$pq^2(1+q)$	$\frac{1}{4}q^2(1+q)^2$	1.00
Obs. no.	45	53	78	3	36	29	244
Exp. no.	44.4	51.5	75.3	7.5	39.4	25.9	244

The expected frequencies and numbers are then calculated in the usual manner. It is seen that the agreement between the observed and calculated numbers is very good.

When there is dominance, there are only three types of sib pairs with the following frequencies (obtained from pooling certain combinations of Table 3-6):

$$\text{Dom, dom:} \quad S_{11} = 1 - S_{10} - S_{00} = 1 - q^2 - \tfrac{1}{2}S_{10}$$
$$\text{Dom, rec:} \quad S_{10} = \tfrac{1}{2}pq^2(3 + q)$$
$$\text{Rec, rec:} \quad S_{00} = \tfrac{1}{4}q^2(1 + q)^2 \quad = q^2 - \tfrac{1}{2}S_{10}$$

Since many hereditary traits in man have dominance, these

frequencies are of value in certain types of research. We shall have occasion to refer to them later (Chap. 8).

Other Relatives

Consider the parent X_1X_2. The probability that his child will inherit X_1 is $\frac{1}{2}$, and the probability that his grandchild will also inherit X_1 is $\frac{1}{4}$, and so on. When the relationship between two relatives becomes remote, the probability that they share a common gene (identical by descent) becomes very small. It is for this reason that we shall dispense with detailed discussions of other relatives. Those who are interested in this subject may refer to Cotterman (1947) or Li (1955a).

The estimation of gene frequencies from groups of family members has only been crudely treated here. Those who are interested in the most efficient estimation method, based on the principle of maximum likelihood, may consult Fisher (1940), Cotterman (1947), and Finney (1948).

The genetic relationship of family members with respect to sex-linked genes has been given in some detail by Li and Sacks (1954), using the *ITO* method.

Chapter 4

Multiple Alleles and Blood Types

The number of alleles at any given locus is by no means limited to two; there could be three, four, or more and then they are called *multiple* alleles. In fact, the MN locus, the Rh locus, the sickle hemoglobin locus, all of which have been mentioned in previous chapters, involve multiple alleles. In this chapter, we shall extend the previous family and population laws and methods of analysis to cases of multiple alleles.

The Sickle Hemoglobin Locus

The number of alleles at this locus is still a matter for study, but it has been shown definitely that there are at least three. In addition to the normal adult hemoglobin (A) and the sickle hemoglobin (S), there is a third, known as hemoglobin type C and also considered abnormal. A formal notation for the series of three alleles is Hb^A, Hb^S, Hb^C, for good reasons. For our purpose here, we shall informally write only the superscripts A, S, C, with the understanding that they are the alleles of the Hb locus.

One of the main difficulties in studying multiple alleles in man is to demonstrate that they are actually alleles. Not all populations have all three alleles. Allele S may be abundant in an African population that lacks C completely. A South Asian population may have C but no S. To prove allelism, all three must be present in the same family which segregates. The allelism of A, S, C is proved by the rare occurrence of the following types of families:

44

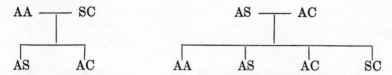

Proof of allelism is time-consuming when the allele in question is rare in the population, because we just have to wait for the right family with a fairly large number of children. In the hemoglobin case, it is fortunate that all six genotypes (AA, AS, SS, AC, SC, CC) can be distinguished by filter-paper electrophoresis (see, e.g., Ranney, 1954). Dominance greatly complicates the task of proving allelism.

For a population in which all three alleles are present, the genotypic proportions are given by an obvious extension of the Hardy-Weinberg law. Let p, q, r denote the frequencies of the alleles A, S, C, respectively. Then the six genotypic proportions are the terms of $(p + q + r)^2$. For example, if $p = .95$, $q = .04$, $r = .01$, the population will consist of:

Genotype:	AA	AS	AC	SS	SC	CC	Total
Proportion:	p^2	$2pq$	$2pr$	q^2	$2qr$	r^2	1.00
Example:	.9025	.0760	.0190	.0016	.0008	.0001	1.00

This example represents roughly the situation in American Negroes. When there is no dominance, the estimation of the gene frequencies follows the same procedure as that for the MN system, described in Chap. 3. Let n_{AA} be the observed number of AA individuals, etc., and G the total number in a random sample from the population. The estimate of the frequency of the A allele and its variance are:

$$p = \frac{2n_{AA} + n_{AS} + n_{AC}}{2G} \qquad V(p) = \frac{p(1 - p)}{2G}$$

The estimates of q and r take the same form. The formula above applies to all cases without dominance.

The frequency of the various types of mating is calculated in the manner shown in Chap. 2. For instance,

AS × AC: freq = $2(2pq)(2pr)$ = 2(.076)(.019) = .002,888
AA × SC: freq = $2(p^2)(2qr)$ = 2(.9025)(.0008) = .001,444

The former type of mating is *always* twice as frequent as the latter, whatever the gene frequency. In our particular example, the total frequency of these two types of families is only about four per thousand.

Suppose that a number of AA × SC families have been observed and their total offspring consist in a individuals with S hemoglobin and b with C hemoglobin. We may wish to test whether these numbers conform with the expected 1:1 ratio. The chi square for this test is, writing $a + b = n$,

$$\chi^2 = \frac{(a - \frac{1}{2}n)^2}{\frac{1}{2}n} + \frac{(b - \frac{1}{2}n)^2}{\frac{1}{2}n} = \frac{(a - b)^2}{n}$$

with one degree of freedom. Similarly, if a number of AS × AC families have been observed and their total offspring consist in a individuals with A hemoglobin (AA or AS or AC) and b without (i.e., SC), the chi square for testing the expected 3:1 ratio is:

$$\chi^2 = \frac{(a - 3b)^2}{3n}$$

with one degree of freedom. These tests for Mendelian ratios are possible only when the genotypes of both parents are known.

The ABO Blood Groups

This is probably the best-known series of multiple alleles in man, and hence we shall not describe the antigen-antibody relationship here because it has been so admirably explained and illustrated in most textbooks of general genetics and human genetics. The ABO locus has also three (major) alleles, a formal notation for which is I^A, I^B, I^O. Again, for the sake of simplicity, we shall only write the superscripts A, B, O, with the locus identification symbol I understood. Now the reader may appreciate why the formal notation is necessary: the A of the ABO series has nothing to do with the A of the ASC series.

The ABO locus is more susceptible of gene frequency analysis on the population level than the hemoglobin locus, because all three alleles are usually present in all populations and none of them is too rare. There are exceptions; for instance, some American Indian and Australian populations have only A and O but no B. There is, however, a complication. Whereas all the six genotypes of the hemoglobin series are distinguishable, this is not the case with ABO. In the latter series, both A and B are dominant over O, but AB individuals have antigen A as well as antigen B (*codominant*). Consequently, there are only four distinguishable phenotypes (i.e., blood groups). To emphasize the symmetrical nature of the four blood groups, the six genotypes can be arranged in a triangular pattern, as shown in the left of Fig. 4-1, in which the three homozygotes are at the bottom and

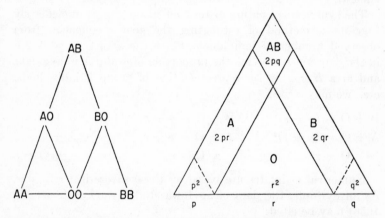

FIG. 4-1. Diagrammatic representation of the ABO system. Left: arrangement of the six genotypes. Right: the gene frequencies are represented by the segments of the base, and the genotypic proportions are represented by the areas of triangles and parallelograms.

each heterozygote is at the vertex of a triangle with the two corresponding homozygotes at its base. To have a quantitative representation of the genotypic proportions, an equilateral triangle may be drawn with the base subdivided into three segments proportional in length to $p:r:q$. From such points of segmentation, lines parallel to both sides are drawn. The resulting areas of the three equilateral triangles on the base represent the frequencies of the three homozygotes (p^2, r^2, q^2), and the three parallelograms represent the three heterozygotes $(2pr, 2pq, 2qr)$. The combined area of AA and AO represents the frequency of group A and, similarly, BB and BO represent group B.

For ease of drawing, it is assumed in Fig. 4-1 that $p = .20$, $r = .60$, $q = .20$, roughly representing the situation of an Asian population with comparatively high B frequency. In a Western European population the gene frequencies are roughly $p = .30$, $r = .60$, $q = .10$. The difference in the values of p and q is more pronounced than that in r. In either case, a glance at the triangular diagram shows that most of the individuals of groups A and B are heterozygotes on account of the high frequency of allele O.

The symmetrical nature of the four blood groups immediately suggests a method of estimating the gene frequencies from observed number of individuals. Since the area $A = p^2 + 2pr$ in the diagram represents the proportion of group A individuals, and area $B = q^2 + 2qr$ represents that of group B individuals, etc., we may write:

$$B + O = (q + r)^2 \quad \sqrt{B + O} = q + r \quad 1 - \sqrt{B + O} = p$$
$$A + O = (p + r)^2 \quad \sqrt{A + O} = p + r \quad 1 - \sqrt{A + O} = q$$
$$O = r^2 \quad \sqrt{O} = r \quad \sqrt{O} = r$$

Numerical estimates are based on these theoretical relations. As an example, the data of an Iowa study (Buckwalter et al., 1956) may be cited:

AB, 61   A, 672   B, 147   0, 743   Total, 1,623

It is desirable to perform the arithmetic systematically according

TABLE 4-1. THE ESTIMATION OF ABO GENE FREQUENCIES
FROM 1,623 INDIVIDUALS IN IOWA

Blood group	Observed number	Proportion	$\sqrt{Proportion}$	First estimate	Adjusting factor	Adjusted estimate	Standard error
B + O	890	0.5484	0.7405	$.2595 = p'$	.9988	$.2592 = p$	.0083
A + O	1,415	.8718	.9337	$.0663 = q'$	.9988	$.0662 = q$	.0044
O	743	.4578	.6766	$.6766 = r'$	See text	$.6746 = r$	.0089
Total..	1,623	......	......	1.0024	....	1.0000	

to the algebraic expressions shown above. The details are given in Table 4-1. The first five columns of Table 4-1 need no explanation, except to note that the sum of the first estimates is 1.0024 instead of unity. Apparently each estimate should be diminished slightly so they would add up to unity. Let $d = .0024$, the deviation from unity. The adjusting factor for p' and q' is

$$1 - \tfrac{1}{2}d = 1 - .0012 = .9988$$

so the adjusted estimate

$$p = p'(1 - \tfrac{1}{2}d) = .2595 \times .9988 = .2592$$

etc. The adjustment for r' is a little different, being:

$$r = (r' - \tfrac{1}{2}d)(1 - \tfrac{1}{2}d) = (.6754)(.9988) = .6746$$

The adjusted estimates now add up to unity. If they do not, a second round of adjustment may be performed but usually this is unnecessary. The adjustment method is due to Bernstein (1930). For all practical purposes, the adjusted estimates may be accepted as the maximum likelihood solutions (Stevens, 1938).

Let us recall that, if allele A were dominant over all other alleles, the variance of the estimate of its frequency would be:

$$V(p) = \frac{p(1 - p)}{2G} + \frac{p^2}{4G} = \frac{(.2592)(.7408)}{2(1623)} + \frac{(.2592)^2}{4(1623)}$$
$$= 69.50 \times 10^{-6}$$

The first component, $p(1 - p)/2G$, represents the variance when there is no dominance and the number of alleles in a sample is known; therefore, it is the minimum variance of any sample estimate. Now, the A in the ABO system is like a complete dominant allele most of the time, except in genotype AB, which consists of 3.76 per cent of the individuals in our sample. The variance of p (maximum likelihood solution) is slightly smaller than the one indicated above, being (DeGroot, 1956; Li, 1956b):

$$V(p) = \frac{p(1 - p)}{2G} + \frac{p^2}{8G}\left(1 + \frac{r}{pq + r}\right)$$
$$V(q) = \frac{q(1 - q)}{2G} + \frac{q^2}{8G}\left(1 + \frac{r}{pq + r}\right)$$

The factor $r/(pq + r)$ is equal to 0.9752 in our example, so $V(p) = 69.37 \times 10^{-6}$ and $V(q) = 19.71 \times 10^{-6}$. In most human populations the value of $r/(pq + r)$ is larger than .90 and in many cases larger than .95, so the approximate and exact expressions for variance differ only very slightly, as illustrated by our example. The variance of r is:

$$V(r) = \frac{r(1 - r)}{2G} + \frac{(1 - r)^2}{8G} + \frac{r(p - q)^2}{8G(pq + r)} = 78.58 \times 10^{-6}$$

The square root of the variance is given in the last column of Table 4-1.

The frequencies of various types of mating and their offspring, of mother-child combinations, and of sib-sib pairs have all been given in detail elsewhere (Li, 1955a, Chap. 4). The traditional method of arriving at those results is long and tedious, but they can be achieved at one step by the *ITO* method explained in Chap. 3.

Subgroups of A

The major allele A consists of two alleles A_1 and A_2, the former being dominant to the latter. Let p_1 and p_2 denote the frequency of A_1 and A_2, so that $p = p_1 + p_2$ is the frequency of A. As an exercise, the reader may arrange the ten genotypes into a triangular pattern with the four homozygotes (A_1A_1, A_2A_2, OO, BB) at the base and draw a corresponding equilateral triangle to represent the genotypic proportions in exactly the same manner as shown in Fig. 4-1. He will then find that the six phenotypes have the following frequencies:

A_1B $2p_1q$	A_2B $2p_2q$	B (BB + BO) $q^2 + 2qr$	
A_1 ($A_1A_1 + A_1A_2 + A_1O$) $p_1^2 + 2p_1p_2 + 2p_1r$	A_2 ($A_2A_2 + A_2O$) $p_2^2 + 2p_2r$	O (OO) r^2	$(p + r)^2$

$$\underbrace{p_2^2 + 2p_2(q + r) \qquad (q + r)^2}_{(p_2 + q + r)^2}$$

Note that B and O groups remain the same; AB and A are each split into two subgroups:

$$AB = A_1B + A_2B = 2p_1q + 2p_2q = 2pq$$
$$A = A_1 + A_2 = (p_1 + p_2)^2 + 2(p_1 + p_2)r = p^2 + 2pr$$

The symmetrical nature still remains; hence the method of estimating the gene frequencies follows the same general procedure as in the case of three alleles. Ignoring the subgroups, we may estimate p; and pooling $A_2B + A_2$ and $B + O$, we may estimate p_1. Then p_2 is obtained by subtraction. In brief, the estimation is based on the following theoretical relations (Mourant, 1954, p. 219):

$$\left. \begin{array}{l} p_1 = 1 - \sqrt{A_2B + A_2 + B + O} \\ p_2 = \sqrt{A_2B + A_2 + B + O} - \sqrt{B + O} \end{array} \right\} \begin{array}{l} p = 1 - \sqrt{B + O} \\ q = 1 - \sqrt{A + O} \\ r = \sqrt{O} \end{array}$$

Table 4-2 gives a numerical example. The first five columns (up to first estimates) are done according to the algebraic expressions

TABLE 4-2. THE ESTIMATION OF A_1A_2BO GENE FREQUENCIES

Sample	A_1B,	4	A_2B	2	B	29	35
	A_1	124	A_2	26	O	160	310
		128		28		189	345

Group	Number	Prop.	$\sqrt{Prop.}$	First estimate	Adj. factor	Adj. estimate	Standard error
$A_2B + A_2 + B + O$	217	.6290	.7931	$.2069 = p_1'$	1.0035	$.2076 = p_1$	.0164
$B + O$	189	.5478	.7401	$.0530 = p_2'$	1.0035	$.0532 = p_2$	.0097
$A + O$	310	.8985	.9479	$.0521 = q'$	1.0035	$.0523 = q$	.0086
O	160	.4638	.6810	$.6810 = r'$	......	$.6869 = r$	.0190
Total..............	345	.....	.....	.9930	......	1.0000	

above; for instance, $p_2' = .7931 - .7401 = .0530$. The sum of these first estimates is .9930; its deviation from unity is $d = .9930 - 1 = -.0070$. Each estimate should be increased slightly so they will add up to unity. The method of adjustment is the same as before; thus,

$$p_1 = p_1'(1 - \tfrac{1}{2}d) = .2069 \times 1.0035 = .2076$$

etc., and:

$$r = (r' - \tfrac{1}{2}d)(1 - \tfrac{1}{2}d) = .6845 \times 1.0035 = .6869$$

The adjusted estimates now add up to unity and for all practical purposes may be regarded as the maximum likelihood solutions. The variance of p_1 is obtained by substituting p_1 for p in the previous formula:

$$V(p_1) = \frac{p_1(1 - p_1)}{2G} + \frac{p_1^2}{8G}\left(1 + \frac{r}{p_1 q + r}\right)$$

while the expressions for $V(q)$ and $V(r)$ remain the same as before with $p = p_1 + p_2$. The only problem is $V(p_2)$, because allele A_2 is recessive to A_1 but behaves like the ordinary A of the three-allele case to B and O. The author finds the following expression quite satisfactory:

$$V(p_2) = \frac{p_2(1 - p_2)}{2G(1 - p_1)} + \frac{p_2^2}{8G(1 - p_1)^2}\left(1 + \frac{r}{p_2 q + r}\right)$$

It is the same formula for $V(p)$, except that $2G$ is multiplied by $(1 - p_1)$ in the first component and $8G$ is multiplied by $(1 - p_1)^2$ in the second component. The numerical values are as follows, and the reader is urged to perform the arithmetic himself.

$$V(p_1) = 2.694 \times 10^{-4} \qquad V(p_2) = 0.954 \times 10^{-4}$$
$$V(q) = 0.738 \times 10^{-4} \qquad V(r) = 3.627 \times 10^{-4}$$

The standard errors are given in the last column of Table 4-2. The method of adjustment and the variance formula for the A_1A_2BO system described in this section do not seem to have been fully investigated by biometricians. The estimates and their variances obtained for this example are identical (within the limit of rounding-off errors) with those obtained by Stevens (1938) through the formal procedure of maximum likelihood.

The MNS System

The two-allele MN system has been mentioned several times in earlier chapters. In fact, this locus also has a series of multiple alleles. The three genotypes (MM, MN, NN) are distinguished by anti-M and anti-N sera. If a third type of serum (anti-S) is used, each genotype may be further identified as S positive or S negative. Each of the major alleles M and N consists of two alleles (analogous to $A = A_1 + A_2$), one yielding S-positive reaction and one S-negative. These four alleles may be designated by MS, Ms, NS, Ns and their respective frequencies by m_1, m_2, n_1, n_2, so $m = m_1 + m_2$ is the frequency of the major allele M and $n = n_1 + n_2$ is the frequency of N. Furthermore, the alleles MS and NS are dominant to Ms and Ns with respect to the S reaction (but there is no dominance with respect to the MN reactions). Hence, with respect to the S reaction, $s = m_2 + n_2$ is the total frequency of the recessive alleles Ms and Ns. The situation may be summarized as follows:

MS m_1	NS n_1	$m_1 + n_1 = 1 - s$
Ms m_2	Ns n_2	$m_2 + n_2 = \phantom{1 - {}} s$
M $\quad m$	N $\quad n$	1.00

On account of the dominance in S reaction, there are only six phenotypes, because each of the M, MN, N types is subdivided into S positive and negative. In the upper portion of Table 4-3 are the theoretical proportions of the six phenotypes (MS, etc.) and general notation for observed numbers (D_1, etc.); in the lower portion is a numerical example showing the arithmetic procedure of estimating the gene frequencies. The frequencies of the major alleles M and N are estimated first by the usual method:

$$m = \frac{2G_1 + G_2}{2G} \qquad n = \frac{G_2 + 2G_3}{2G}$$

TABLE 4-3. UPPER PORTION: THEORETICAL PROPORTIONS OF THE SIX
PHENOTYPES OF THE MNS SYSTEM (D_1, D_2, D_3 ARE OBSERVED
NUMBERS); LOWER PORTION: NUMERICAL EXAMPLE OF
ESTIMATING THE GENE FREQUENCIES

MS $m_1^2 + 2m_1m_2$ D_1	MNS $2(m_1n_1 + m_1n_2 + m_2n_1)$ D_2	NS $n_1^2 + 2n_1n_2$ D_3	S positive $1 - (m_2 + n_2)^2 = 1 - s^2$ D
Ms m_2^2 R_1	MNs $2m_2n_2$ R_2	Ns n_2^2 R_3	S negative $(m_2 + n_2)^2 = s^2$ R
m^2 G_1	$2mn$ G_2	n^2 G_3	1.00 G
(MS) 44 (Ms) 35	(MNS) 62 (MNs) 47	(NS) 21 (Ns) 21	$D = 127$ $1 - s^2 = D/G = 0.5522$ $R = 103$ $s^2 = R/G = 0.4478$
(M) 79	(MN) 109	(N) 42	$G = 230$ 1.0000

Estimation

$$m = \frac{2(79) + 109}{2(230)} = 0.5804 \qquad n = \frac{109 + 2(42)}{2(230)} = 0.4196 \qquad s = \sqrt{\frac{R}{G}} = 0.6692$$

$$m_2 = \frac{2(35) + 47}{2(103)} s = 0.3801 \qquad n_2 = \frac{47 + 2(21)}{2(103)} s = 0.2891 \qquad m_2n_2 = 0.1099$$

$$m_1 = m - m_2 = 0.2003 \qquad n_1 = n - n_2 = 0.1305 \qquad m_2^2(1 - s^2) = 0.07978$$

$$m_2 - m_1 = 0.1798 \qquad\qquad n_2 - n_1 = 0.1586 \qquad\qquad n_2^2(1 - s^2) = 0.04615$$

$$n(m_2 - m_1) = 0.07544 \qquad m(n_2 - n_1) = 0.09205$$

The total frequency of the recessive alleles Ms and Ns may again
be estimated by the usual formula:

$$s^2 = R/G \qquad s = m_2 + n_2 = \sqrt{R/G}$$

From the theoretical proportions of the three S-recessive phenotypes (Ms, MNs, Ns) it is obvious that the relative magnitude
of m_2 and n_2 is in the ratio:

$$m_2 : n_2 = \frac{2R_1 + R_2}{2R} : \frac{R_2 + 2R_3}{2R}$$

But $m_2 + n_2 = s$, hence (DeGroot and Li, 1960):

$$m_2 = \left(\frac{2R_1 + R_2}{2R}\right) s \qquad n_2 = \left(\frac{R_2 + 2R_3}{2R}\right) s$$

The values of m_1 and n_1 may then be obtained by subtraction. This is the arithmetic procedure shown in the lower portion of Table 4-3. The other values shown in the table ($m_2 - m_1$, $n_2 - n_1$, $m_2 n_2$, etc.) are needed for calculating the variances, of which the formulas are:

$$V(m_2) = \frac{m_2 n_2}{2R} + \frac{m_2^2 (1 - s^2)}{4R} \qquad V(m_1) = V(m_2) - \frac{n(m_2 - m_1)}{2G}$$

$$V(n_2) = \frac{m_2 n_2}{2R} + \frac{n_2^2 (1 - s^2)}{4R} \qquad V(n_1) = V(n_2) - \frac{m(n_2 - n_1)}{2G}$$

Substituting the numerical values of $m_2 n_2$, etc., shown in Table 4-3, the reader will find the following results:

Estimate:	m_2	m_1	n_2	n_1
Variance:	7.27	5.63	6.45	4.45, each $\times 10^{-4}$
S.D.	.0270	.0237	.0254	.0211

The method of estimation given here is marked for its extreme simplicity; also, explicit expressions for variances are known. Although the method is not fully efficient and may fail for very small samples, the estimates as well as their variances for this example of 230 individuals are practically identical with those obtained by Boyd (1954) through the formal procedure of maximum likelihood.

An interesting method of iterative counting of the genes has been developed by Ceppellini, Siniscalco, and Smith (1955) and further improved by Smith (1957) as a means of estimating gene frequency. The successive estimates obtained by this numerical procedure converge to those obtained by the maximum likelihood method and are, therefore, fully efficient.

Racial Intermixture

The study of gene frequencies has many applications, one of which is to trace the origin and to ascertain the degree of intermixture of human races. The information on gene frequency has been extensively used by some physical anthropologists. However, not all the anthropological applications are valid on account of the selective forces that tend to change the gene frequency in due time. The subject of selection and change in gene frequency will be discussed in Chap. 9. If the change in gene frequency per generation due to selection is not too great, and if we study a short-term phenomenon instead of trying to draw conclusions about an event that happened three or four thousand years ago, the gene frequency analysis would be very useful. Of all the racial intermixtures in human history, probably the greatest is that between the American Negro and white populations in the last 10 generations, and it is the one most suitable for genetic analysis.

A hybrid between a Negro and a white person is socially regarded as a Negro (biologically half and half, of course). Henceforth, the American white population will be referred to as the *base population* and the American Negro population as the *hybrid population*. Genes from the base population "flow" into the hybrid population but not vice versa (ignoring the very few that "passed" for white). In calculating the rate of this "gene flow," it is most reliable to use the frequency of a locus that differs very widely in the two populations. Glass and Li (1953) use the R_0 frequencies as well as some others as a basis for calculation. (The Rh locus, mentioned before elsewhere, consists in a series of multiple alleles so complicated that it is beyond the comprehension of nonprofessional immunologists, and new alleles still continue to be discovered every so often. R_0 is one of the eight major alleles of the locus.) The frequency of R_0 in the three populations concerned are as follows:

American whites (base)	East Africa (original)	American Negro (hybrid)
$Q = .028$	$q_0 = .630$	$q_k = .446$

We shall assume that both Q and q_0 remain constant in the last few generations and only q_k changes due to gene flow. Let m be the fraction of the hybrid population R_0 genes that is derived from American whites through interbreeding in each generation. Then, after the first generation of interbreeding, the R_0 frequency of the resulting hybrid population will be changed from q_0 to:

$$q_1 = (1 - m)q_0 + mQ$$

Since the original gene frequency is diluted by a factor of $1 - m$ each generation, the gene frequency in the hybrid population will be:

$$q_k = (1 - m)^k q_0 + [1 - (1 - m)^k]Q$$

after k generations of interbreeding. Solving for m in terms of the known values of q_0, q_k, and Q, we have:

$$(1 - m)^k = \frac{q_k - Q}{q_0 - Q} = \frac{.446 - .028}{.630 - .028} = .694$$

Appreciable intermixture between Negroes and whites probably began in the middle of the seventeenth century (approximately 275 to 300 years ago). If we take this period as 10 generations ($k = 10$), then $m = .0358$, or 3.58 per cent per generation. Since the remaining percentage of original Negro genes is $(1 - m)^k = 69.4$ per cent, the total accumulated intermixture of white genes over the period of 10 generations is $1 - .694 = .306$. In other words, the American Negro is, genetically speaking, 30 per cent white. Similar calculations based on frequencies of some other loci yield approximately the same conclusion. The estimate of the percentage for white genes in the American Negro population varies from 25 to 35 per cent.

Chapter 5

Index Case and Recessive Proportion

The study of genetic segregation in man, as outlined in this chapter, deals with the recessive proportion of children from parents of specified (heterozygous) genotypes. This problem has nothing to do with the gene frequencies in the population. The methodology outlined below is applicable to all recessive traits. whether common or rare.

Before taking up the subject of finding the correct proportion of recessives in human families, let us make certain that the reader is able to handle the following type of problems. One example should suffice, but two are given to ensure familiarity with the subject.

Problem 1. A number of planes were sent over an enemy area, and it was reported that $\frac{2}{5}$ of them have been destroyed. Only 42 planes have returned safely. What is the total number of planes sent out?

Let c be the total number of planes originally sent out. Since $\frac{2}{5}$ of them are missing, the 42 planes that came back must represent $1 - \frac{2}{5} = \frac{3}{5}$ of the total. Hence we obtain the equation:

$$(1 - \tfrac{2}{5})c = 42$$

Hence, $$c = \frac{42}{1 - \frac{2}{5}} = \frac{42}{\frac{3}{5}} = 42 \times \tfrac{5}{3} = 70$$

Problem 2. One snowy morning $\frac{27}{64}$ of the registered students of a freshman chemistry class were stranded at home, and only 111 students showed up for the class. What is the total number of students registered for the chemistry course?

Let c be the total number of students registered. Since $27/64$ of them were absent, the 111 students in the classroom must represent $1 - 27/64 = 37/64$ of the total. Hence the equation:

$$(1 - 27/64)c = 111$$

$$\therefore c = \frac{111}{1 - 27/64} = \frac{111}{37/64} = 111 \times 64/37 = 192$$

The problem in either case is to find the total when a fraction of it is missing and only the remaining portion has been observed. A similar situation arises in the study of human genetics owing to the peculiar method of collecting human data.

Segregation in Small Families

When the three genotypes (AA, Aa, aa) are all distinguishable, there will be no special difficulty in studying the segregation in human families even though the size of family is very small (for genetic study purposes). For instance, although each Aa × Aa family has only a few children, we may study a large number of such families and see if there are $\frac{1}{4}$AA, $\frac{1}{2}$Aa, $\frac{1}{4}$aa among their *total* children. When there is dominance, however, the dominant × dominant type of family is a mixture of three genotypic types of families (AA × AA, AA × Aa, Aa × Aa), two of which cannot produce a recessive child. Hence the segregation of the Aa × Aa family cannot be studied straightforwardly by first identifying the parents.

If the frequency of the recessive gene is low in the population, the great majority of families are of the dominant × dominant type, so the method of *population ratio*, described in Chap. 3, becomes unfeasible. Furthermore, the great majority of the recessives are from Aa × Aa parents. Under these circumstances we resort to the principle of the *progeny test* as employed by plant and animal geneticists. The method is to identify the parental genotypes not by examining their phenotypes but by examining their offspring. Thus, if both parents are normal (dominant phenotype) and yet they have one or more recessive (e.g., albino) children, this implies that both parents are heterozygous (Aa). It is through the presence of one or more recessive offspring that Aa × Aa matings may be identified from the other two types.

Unfortunately, the identification of Aa × Aa parents through the presence of one or more recessive offspring is only partially successful, because of the small size of human families. To illustrate the point, let us consider Aa × Aa families with three children. The probability that a child is normal (dominant phenotype) is $\frac{3}{4}$ and that he is recessive is $\frac{1}{4}$. With three children, there are four possible types of sibship, viz., those with 0, 1, 2, 3 recessive members among the three children. The probabilities for such sibships are the terms of:

$$(\tfrac{3}{4} + \tfrac{1}{4})^3 = (\tfrac{3}{4})^3 + 3(\tfrac{3}{4})^2(\tfrac{1}{4}) + 3(\tfrac{3}{4})(\tfrac{1}{4})^2 + (\tfrac{1}{4})^3$$
$$= \frac{(27 + 27 + 9 + 1)}{64}$$

Figure 5-1 provides a visual representation of this situation. We note that $(\tfrac{3}{4})^3$, or 27 of the 64 families, produce no recessive

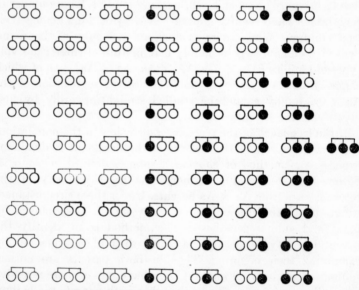

Fig. 5-1. Segregation of a simple recessive trait (solid symbol) in families of three children when both parents are heterozygous.

offspring, and thus the parents cannot be identified as Aa $\times$ Aa by the progeny test. These families are superficially no different from the other two types of normal families that constitute the majority of the population. The recessive child through whom the parents are identified and thus included in our study record is known as the *index case* or *propositus* or *proband*. Thus, the index method can only identify $1 - (\frac{3}{4})^3 = 1 - \frac{27}{64} = \frac{37}{64}$ of the true Aa $\times$ Aa families with three children. The same situation is true for families of any size, and this is the major source of the difficulty in studying human segregation.

The Direct A Priori Correction

Let us examine the idealized situation of Fig. 5-1 once more. The 64 families have a total of $3 \times 64 = 192$ children, of whom 48 are recessive, so the proportion of recessives is $\frac{48}{192} = \frac{1}{4}$, as it should be. Now, if we omit the 27 families without a recessive child from the picture, the remaining 37 families have $3 \times 37 = 111$ children, of whom 48 are recessive, so the proportion of recessives becomes $\frac{48}{111}$, or approximately 43 per cent, which is much higher than the correct 25 per cent. The omission of the 27 apparently normal families (necessitated by the index method) has introduced a tremendous upward bias in estimating the segregation ratio. Further, we note that this bias arises not from the total number of recessive children (which is 48 in both cases) but from the diminished number of families and the corresponding number of total children. So much is clear from the mere inspection of Fig. 5-1.

The method of correcting the bias is simple. Since $(\frac{3}{4})^3$ of the families are missed and the 111 children from the remaining families with at least one recessive offspring represent $1 - (\frac{3}{4})^3$ of the theoretical total, the latter must be equal to (see Problem 2 at the beginning of the chapter):

$$c = \frac{111}{1 - (\frac{3}{4})^3} = 192$$

The proportion of recessives calculated on the basis of $c = 192$ children will be unbiased. That is, $48/c = \frac{1}{4}$. The correction method is simply to restore the number of children to its theoretical total $c = 192$ on the basis of the observed portion $t = 111$. The argument for families of three children may be applied to families of any other size. For instance, when the size of sibship is four (the distribution of the five types of sibships has been given on page 11), the corresponding correction factor is $1 - (\frac{3}{4})^4 = 1 - \frac{81}{256} = \frac{175}{256}$. In general, for sibships of size s, the correction factor is:

$$1 - (\tfrac{3}{4})^s = \frac{4^s - 3^s}{4^s}$$

The correction method, however, does not apply to families with a single child ($s = 1$) who is necessarily a recessive. The correction factor for such a case is $1 - \frac{3}{4} = \frac{1}{4}$, so for each recessive child the corrected total number of children is always four. It may be shown that such families yield no information on the segregation ratio, and hence, in practice, single-child families are excluded from analysis.

The most important requirement of this method is that the number of families of a given size (s) containing 1, 2, 3, or more recessive children (chosen through the index cases) are really proportional to the terms of $(\frac{3}{4} + \frac{1}{4})^s$ with the first term truncated. Thus, for families of three children ($s = 3$), the number of sibships with 1, 2, 3 recessives should be proportional to 27, 9, 1. Similarly, for families of four children ($s = 4$), the number of sibships containing 1, 2, 3, 4 recessives should be proportional to 108, 54, 12, 1. When all the families with at least one recessive child in a community are observed, this condition is naturally satisfied. For this reason, this method is applicable to the case of *complete ascertainment* or *complete selection*. Theoretically, as long as the families are chosen randomly as units, that is, any family with at least one recessive child is equally likely to be observed and included in our record, this method is appropriate. But the assumption that families with one or more recessive children have the same chance of being recorded is hardly true in practice except in the case of complete ascertainment. This question will be discussed in a later section.

An Example

An example is given in Table 5-1 to illustrate how the method works in combining families of all sizes and at the same time to introduce a few symbols that shall be needed in later discussions. Sjögren's data (1943) are based on almost complete ascertainment, so the direct a priori method is appropriate. The disease, Friedreich's ataxia, is hereditary and apparently recessive in nature, since the parents of the patients are all normal. Table 5-1

TABLE 5-1. THE A PRIORI CORRECTION METHOD APPLIED
TO SJÖGREN'S (1943) DATA ON THE INHERITANCE
OF FRIEDREICH'S ATAXIA

Size of sibship s	Number of sibships n_s	Number of children $sn_s = t_s$	Observed no. of ataxias r_s	Theoretical total children $c_s = \dfrac{t_s}{1 - (\frac{3}{4})^s}$	Corrected prop. of ataxias $b_s = \dfrac{r_s}{c_s}$
2	8	16	9	36.5	.247
3	11	33	14	57.1	.245
4	9	36	11	52.7	.209
5	9	45	14	59.0	.237
6	7	42	15	51.1	.294
Total....	44	172	63	256.4	.2457
	$N = \Sigma n_s$	$T = \Sigma t_s$	$R = \Sigma r_s$	$C = \Sigma c_s$	$b = R/C$

reproduces only part of Sjögren's collection; the families with seven or more children are omitted for the sake of simplicity. Consider the 11 families with $3 \times 11 = 33$ children. Each of these families has at least one ataxic child, and there are altogether 14 ataxia cases among the 11 families. The restored theoretical total number of children is then $c_3 = 33/(1 - (\frac{3}{4})^3) = 57.1$. We apply this correction separately to families of each fixed size and then add the corrected total number of children together. It is seen that without correction the combined proportion of recessives is $R/T = 63/172 = 36.6$ per cent, and the corrected proportion is:

$$b = \frac{R}{C} = \frac{\Sigma r_s}{\Sigma c_s} = \frac{63}{256.4} = 0.2457$$

which is very close to the theoretical Mendelian proportion .250.

To test the agreement between the observed and expected results (or the significance of the difference between them), the numbers or the proportions are used. For instance, in our example, the theoretical grand total number of children is $C = \Sigma c_s = 256.4$, and hence $\frac{1}{4}(256.4) = 64.1$ are expected to be ataxic. The actually observed number is 63. For a significance test we need to know the variance of the observed number of recessives. Alternatively, our pooled estimate of the recessive proportion is $b = .2457$, and we want to compare it with the theoretical .250. In this case we need to know the variance of the estimate b. These variances are simply special cases of a more comprehensive situation to be described in the next section. The author prefers to work with the recessive proportion b so that the results of different investigators from different populations can be directly compared. The number of recessives depends on the number of families included in the study; it varies from study to study.

Estimating the Recessive Proportion

The correction method described in the preceding section is based on the preconceived notion that the probability that a child is dominant is $\frac{3}{4}$ and that he is recessive, $\frac{1}{4}$; hence it is known as the a priori method. Suppose that we do not make this assumption to begin with, and our problem is to find the proportion of the offspring that are recessives. This is a different problem from testing the particular hypothesis $b = \frac{1}{4}$. Let a be the probability that a child is normal (dominant) from two normal heterozygous parents and $b = 1 - a$ the probability that a child is recessive (e.g., suffering from Friedreich's ataxia). The a,b notation has been adopted here instead of the usual p,q notation because we have previously committed the latter to denote the gene frequencies. The value of b (or a) is now an unknown and is to be estimated from the observed data.

The argument and method of correction of the preceding section still hold, except that the fixed number $\frac{3}{4}$ should be replaced by the unknown value $a = 1 - b$. For families of size s, a fraction a^s of the families with heterozygous parents will be missed through the index method. The four columns left of the double line of Table 5-1 are observed data, and they do not change. The only modification necessary is in the c_s column. The restored theoretical total number of children for families of any given size is now $c_s = t_s/(1 - a^s)$. The combined estimate of b from families of all sizes takes the same form as before, viz.,

$$b = \frac{R}{C} = \frac{\Sigma r_s}{\Sigma c_s} = \frac{63}{\sum \left(\dfrac{t_s}{1 - a^s} \right)}$$

On rearrangement, the equation may be written:

$$R = bC = b \sum \left(\frac{n_s s}{1 - a^s} \right) = \sum \left(n_s \cdot \frac{sb}{1 - a^s} \right)$$

Exact solution of the equation for b is very difficult. The usual procedure for solving it is by tedious iteration, starting out with some trial values of b. Here, however, we shall use a much shorter method to obtain an approximate solution, viz., the method of linear interpolation (Lejeune, 1958), with the help of certain tables. From the expression above we see that n_s, the number of families of size s, is the only factor that is determined by the observed data; the other factor, $sb/(1 - a^s)$, can be tabulated once and for all (Table 5-2A).

The arithmetic procedure has been set out in Table 5-3, using the data on Friedreich's ataxia. First, we choose the trial value $b = .225$ and find the sum of products of the observed n_s and the tabulated values of $sb/(1 - a^s)$ to be 61.68, slightly smaller than the observed $R = 63$. Next, we try a larger value of b. With $b = .250$, the expected total number of recessives is found to be 64.10, slightly larger than the observed $R = 63$. [Note that 64.10 is $\frac{1}{4}(256.40)$, as obtained previously by the a priori method.] Hence, the appropriate value of b that will yield 63 recessives

TABLE 5-2A. VALUES OF $\bar{r} = \dfrac{sb}{1 - a^s}$

s	$b = .15$	$b = .20$	$b = .225$	$b = .25$	$b = .275$	$b = .30$	$b = .35$
2	1.081	1.111	1.127	1.143	1.159	1.176	1.212
3	1.166	1.230	1.263	1.297	1.333	1.370	1.448
4	1.255	1.355	1.408	1.463	1.520	1.579	1.704
5	1.348	1.487	1.562	1.639	1.719	1.803	1.980
6	1.445	1.626	1.723	1.825	1.930	2.040	2.271
7	1.545	1.772	1.893	2.020	2.152	2.288	2.576
8	1.649	1.923	2.069	2.223	2.382	2.547	2.892
9	1.757	2.079	2.252	2.433	2.620	2.814	3.217
10	1.868	2.241	2.441	2.649	2.865	3.087	3.548
11	1.982	2.407	2.635	2.871	3.116	3.367	3.884
12	2.098	2.577	2.833	3.098	3.371	3.651	4.224
13	2.218	2.751	3.035	3.329	3.631	3.938	4.567
14	2.341	2.929	3.241	3.563	3.893	4.229	4.912
15	2.465	3.109	3.450	3.801	4.158	4.521	5.258

TABLE 5-2B. VALUES OF $w_s = \dfrac{1}{V(b)_s} = \dfrac{s}{ab} \times \dfrac{1 - a^s - sba^{s-1}}{(1 - a^s)^2}$

s	$b = .15$	$b = .20$	$b = .225$	$b = .25$	$b = .275$	$b = .30$	$b = .35$
2	4.583	3.858	3.640	3.483	3.371	3.295	3.229
3	9.600	8.188	7.774	7.480	7.278	7.149	7.061
4	15.038	12.967	12.367	11.948	11.665	11.489	11.386
5	20.882	18.163	17.380	16.833	16.463	16.230	16.077
6	27.113	23.739	22.761	22.071	21.594	21.279	21.008
7	33.708	29.651	28.458	27.598	26.980	26.545	26.069
8	40.641	35.856	34.415	33.347	32.548	31.947	31.172
9	47.885	42.308	40.578	39.258	38.229	37.416	36.257
10	55.412	48.962	46.896	45.274	43.969	42.898	41.282
11	63.191	55.775	53.322	51.350	49.722	48.356	46.228
12	71.193	62.706	59.815	57.445	55.456	53.762	51.088
13	79.389	69.721	66.341	63.531	61.146	59.103	55.865
14	87.749	76.789	72.873	69.585	66.780	64.372	60.566
15	96.247	83.881	79.387	75.592	72.349	69.568	65.203

must be between .225 and .250. By linear interpolation it is found to be $b^* = .239$, where the asterisk indicates that it is the interpolated solution. That this solution is a very good one may be verified by substituting $b = .239$ and $a = .761$ in the right-hand side of the equation on p. 65, yielding almost exactly 63 recessives.

TABLE 5-3. METHOD OF ESTIMATING THE RECESSIVE PROPORTION AND ITS VARIANCE AMONG SIBSHIPS WITH AT LEAST ONE RECESSIVE MEMBER ON THE ASSUMPTION OF COMPLETE ASCERTAINMENT (DATA FROM TABLE 5-1)

Size of sibship s	Number of sibships n_s	$n_s \times$ entry of Table 5.2A $= n_s \bar{r}_s$		$n_s \times$ entry of Table 5.2B $= n_s w_s$	
		$b = .225$	$b = .250$	$b = .225$	$b = .250$
2	8	9.01	9.14	29.12	27.86
3	11	13.89	14.27	85.51	82.28
4	9	12.67	13.17	111.31	107.53
5	9	14.05	14.75	156.42	151.52
6	7	12.06	12.77	159.35	154.52
Total.....	44	61.68	64.10	541.71	523.71

Linear interpolation
$(R = 63)$
$b^* = .239$ $W^* = 531.6$

The next step is to find the variance of the estimate b. The arithmetic procedure for doing this is exactly the same as that for finding b except that the entries of Table 5-2B are substituted. As indicated in the right-hand portion of Table 5-3, we find that the sum $\Sigma n_s w_s$ for $b = .225$ and $b = .250$ is 541.7 and 523.7, respectively. By linear interpolation we find that the value of $\Sigma n_s w_s = W$ corresponding to $b^* = .239$ is $W^* = 531.6$. Then the variance is:

$$V(b^*) = \frac{1}{W^*} = \frac{1}{531.6} = 0.00188$$

and the standard error of b^* is $\sqrt{.00188} = .043$. The final result may be stated as $b^* = .239 \pm .043$, which is quite in agreement with theoretical $b = .250$.

Thus, the reader has seen that with the help of Tables 5-2A and 5-2B, the estimate b^* and its variance may be obtained in a few minutes. For most practical purposes, this is all the investigator has to do. The meaning of the tabulated $\bar{r}_s$ and w_s is explained in the appendix at the end of the chapter.

Proportional Frequencies

Before taking up another source of bias in collecting human genetic data, we may well digress briefly to say a few words about the class frequencies of a distribution. Let us consider the terms

r	0	1	2	Total
Form 1	$\frac{9}{16}$	$\frac{6}{16}$	$\frac{1}{16}$	1
Form 2	9	6	1	16
Form 3	27	18	3	48
Form 4	.45	.30	.05	0.80

of $(\frac{3}{4} + \frac{1}{4})^2$. Form 1 is the classical one; every term is a probability such that the sum of all the terms is unity. Form 2 describes the same distribution in terms of expected numbers in a total of 16 sibships. In a frequency distribution it is the relative magnitude of the class frequencies that counts. To calculate the mean and variance of r, forms 1 and 2 give us identical results. Hence, the numbers $9:6:1$ may be called *proportional frequencies*. This is, in fact, what we do all the time in everyday conversation. Thus, the distribution $\frac{1}{2}$ and $\frac{1}{2}$ for two classes is referred to as $1:1$, or $50:50$. It follows that form 3 also describes the same distribution $(\frac{3}{4} + \frac{1}{4})^2$. The concept of proportional frequency may be extended even a little further: the total proportional frequency can be any arbitrary number at all, without affecting the mean and variance of the distribution. To emphasize this point, form 4 has been given, which has a total frequency of .80. The reader may satisfy himself by seeing that form 4 yields $\bar{r} = \frac{1}{2}$

and $V(r) = \frac{3}{8}$, the same as those of the other three forms. We shall have an occasion in the appendix to use a form of proportional frequency that does not add up to unity; and this, we have seen, has no effect on the mean and variance of the distribution. For the time being, all the reader should be aware of is that the numbers $27:18:3$ describe the *complete* binomial distribution $(\frac{3}{4} + \frac{1}{4})^2$. Similarly, the proportional frequencies $108:108:36:4 = 27:27:9:1$ are the distribution obtained by expanding $(\frac{3}{4} + \frac{1}{4})^3$. When a binomial distribution is complete, the proportion of recessives may be directly determined by an actual count of recessives and normals, as we did with Fig. 5-1, including families without any recessive child.

Very Incomplete Ascertainment

Now let us consider an entirely different situation from the complete survey of recessive abnormalities in a community. The records of any hospital or physician contain only those patients who come for treatment, and therefore only their families are known to the investigator. Under such circumstances, a family with, say, three recessive abnormalities would be more likely to be detected than a family with only one recessive. Therefore, the sample—the observed number of the various kinds of families— is not "representative" of or proportional to the true distribution of families in the general population. If the ascertainment is very incomplete, it may be shown that the probability of recording a family with r recessives is r times the probability of recording a family of the same size but with only one recessive child. This is a second source of bias. The relation between the distribution of families in population and in sample may be depicted as follows for sibships of sizes $s = 3$ and $s = 4$.

Size of sibship, s Number of recessives, r	$s = 3$ 0 1 2 3	$s = 4$ 0 1 2 3 4
Relative number of families:		
In population	$27:27: 9:1$	$81:108: 54:12:1$
In sample	$0:27:18:3$	$0:108:108:36:4$

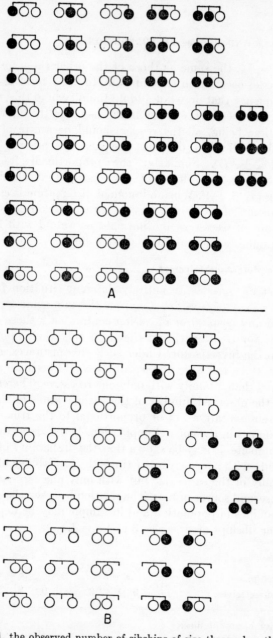

Fig. 5-2. *A*, the observed number of sibships of size three when the probabilities of detecting sibships with two and three recessive members are, respectively, two and three times the probability of detecting a sibship with one recessive. *B*, the method of correction is to delete one recessive member from each sibship, resulting in 24 recessives among a total of 96 children. The recessive proportion is then $\frac{24}{96} = \frac{1}{4}$.

A detailed consideration of the sibships of size three will make our estimation procedure clear. The sibships with two and three recessives are, respectively, two and three times as likely to be detected as the sibship with one recessive. Ignoring families with no recessive (which are not observed), the population distribution $27:9:1$ thus becomes in the sample $27:18:3$. These 48 families are shown in the top portion of Fig. 5-2. It is seen that the proportion of recessives is grossly inflated, being equal to $72/144$.

The method of correcting the inflation is extremely simple. It is recalled that $27:18:3 = 9:6:1$ corresponds to the complete expansion of $(\frac{3}{4} + \frac{1}{4})^2$. Hence, if we regard these sibships of actual size three as if they were of size $s' = s - 1 = 3 - 1 = 2$ by deleting one recessive member from each sibship, we would have obtained a complete binomial distribution with $r' = r - 1 = 0, 1, 2$ recessives. This is done in the lower portion of Fig. 5-2. Actual counting shows that the proportion of recessives is now $24/96 = \frac{1}{4}$ correctly. Since the correction involves the subtraction of one recessive from each of the 48 families, the corrected estimate of the recessive proportion from such families is:

$$b = \frac{72 - 48}{144 - 48} = \frac{24}{96} = \frac{1}{4}$$

Exactly the same situation exists for sibships of size four. The student who encounters this problem for the first time should carry out the arithmetic in detail, as outlined above. In brief, we take the sample distribution $108:108:36:4$ as it is but change $s = 4$ to $s' = 3$ and change $r = 1, 2, 3, 4$ to $r' = 0, 1, 2, 3$. Then we calculate the recessive proportion. It should also be $\frac{1}{4}$.

Example: General Expression

The method of correction outlined above is based on a very fundamental property of the binomial distribution. When the terms of $(a + b)^s$ are each multiplied by the corresponding value of r, the resulting terms are proportional to those of $(a + b)^{s-1}$. In terms of practical arithmetic, all the correction method amounts to is the subtraction of one recessive member from each observed sibship before calculating the recessive proportion. This method applies to sibships of all sizes.

For purpose of illustration, let us consider the data of Table 5-1 once more. There we find that the total number of sibships $N = \Sigma n_s = 44$; the total number of children $T = \Sigma t_s = 172$; and the total number of recessives $R = \Sigma r_s = 63$. If the probability of detecting a sibship is proportional to the number of recessives the sibship contains, then the correct estimate of the recessive proportion is:

$$b = \frac{R - N}{T - N} = \frac{63 - 44}{172 - 44} = \frac{19}{128} = 0.148$$

$$V(b) = \frac{ab}{T - N} = \frac{.852 \times .148}{128} = 0.000988$$

and the standard error of b is $\sqrt{.000988} = .031$. The estimate $b = .15$ is significantly lower than .25. We conclude that either this method of correction is inappropriate for Sjögren's data or Friedreich's ataxia is not a simple Mendelian recessive trait.

Probability of Ascertainment: Practical Difficulties

In the preceding sections we have dealt first with the case of complete ascertainment where the observed number of families of size s form a truncated distribution of $(a + b)^s$ and then dealt with the case of very incomplete ascertainment (also known as *single ascertainment*) where the observed number of families of size s form a complete distribution of $(a + b)^{s-1}$. In each of these two cases we have developed a sound correction method which overcomes the bias in the sample. In practice, however, the situation is frequently in between the two clear-cut extreme cases, and a correct estimate of b is difficult to obtain. In many of the extensive studies made in certain small communities in Western Europe, the situation may be closer to complete ascertainment than to single ascertainment.

The following example illustrates well the deviation of a practical situation from the two ideal cases. In one of the early studies of the inheritance of human albinism the observed distribution of families of size $s = 3$ with at least one albino child is as follows (cited by Haldane, 1938):

Number of albinos in a sibship, r	$s = 3$			Number of families n_3	Number of children $t_3 = 3n_3$	Number of albinos r_3	Corrected number of children c_3
	1	2	3				
Observed number of sibships	37	15	3	55	165	76	$\dfrac{165}{1 - a^3}$
Calculated number:							
(27:9:1)	40.1	13.4	1.5	55			
(9:6:1)	30.9	20.6	3.4	55			

The first set of calculated number of sibships is based on the truncated $(\frac{3}{4} + \frac{1}{4})^3$, assuming complete ascertainment. The second set of calculated number of sibships is based on the complete $(\frac{3}{4} + \frac{1}{4})^2$, assuming single ascertainment. It is at once clear that the actually observed distribution of families is in between the two ideal cases. The estimates of b by the two methods developed above are:

$$\text{Complete ascertainment:} \quad 76 = \frac{165b}{1 - a^3} \qquad b = 0.31$$

$$\text{Single ascertainment:} \quad b = \frac{76 - 55}{165 - 55} = \frac{21}{110} = 0.19$$

This example incidentally brings out another feature of the two estimates. The first estimate, based on complete ascertainment, is usually higher than the expected .25 whereas the second estimate, based on single ascertainment, is usually lower than .25. It is interesting to note that in this particular example the average of the two estimates is $\frac{1}{2}(.31 + .19) = .25$

A more refined analysis of the intermediate situation is not impossible. It involves another parameter known as the *probability of ascertainment*, first introduced by Fisher (1934). To estimate this parameter we need the extra information on the number of times a sibship is being detected independently through its various recessive members. We shall not be able to present such methods on an elementary level. Furthermore, the probability of ascertainment may vary from time to time and from case to case. The problem of arriving at an unbiased estimate of b under incomplete ascertainment has been a happy hunting ground for many mathematical statisticians. Morton (1959) has developed a set of comprehensive formulas, the solution of which requires the service of an IBM 650 computer. Should the geneticist be bewildered in the age of electronics, he may find some comfort in knowing that even C. A. B. Smith (1959), a prominent biometrician, feels that the intermediate cases "will remain for a long time of purely theoretical interest; in practice we can only take the two extreme cases, and assume that our sample lies somewhere between."

APPENDIX

Mean and Variance of r in a Sibship

It is not the purpose of this book to derive variance formulas. However, in view of the fact that the variance of b (as estimated in Estimating the Recessive Proportion on the assumption of complete ascertainment) has been written in various different-looking forms, a certain amount of explanation seems necessary to make the variance formula meaningful and easy to remember. Those who do not care for the algebraic details may well omit this section.

To keep the terminology as simple as possible, we shall continue to speak of sibships of size s with r recessives, instead of using the general statistical language such as r successes in a set of s independent trials. Nevertheless, the reader should be fully aware that the following arguments and results are perfectly general and applicable to estimating the probability of a success in any truncated binomial distribution, in whatever way it may arise. Also, to keep the algebra as simple as possible, we shall proceed from the particular to the general, beginning with binomial distributions of size $s = 3$, as shown in Table 5-4. Case (i) is a complete binomial distribution, and the reader is expected to

TABLE 5-4. MEAN AND VARIANCE OF COMPLETE AND
TRUNCATED BINOMIAL DISTRIBUTIONS

(i) complete $(\frac{3}{4} + \frac{1}{4})^3$				(ii) truncated $(\frac{3}{4} + \frac{1}{4})^3$				(iii) truncated $(a + b)^3$			
r	f	fr	fr^2	r	f	fr	fr^2	r	f	fr	fr^2
0	27	0	0								
1	27	27	27	1	27	27	27	1	$3a^2b$	$3a^2b$	$3a^2b$
2	9	18	36	2	9	18	36	2	$3ab^2$	$6ab^2$	$6ab^2 + 6ab^2$
3	1	3	9	3	1	3	9	3	b^3	$3b^3$	$3b^3 + 6b^3$
Total..	64	48	72	Total.	37	48	72	Total	$1 - a^3$	$3b$	$3b + 6b^2$

$$\text{Mean} = \frac{48}{64} = 0.75 \qquad \bar{r} = \frac{48}{37} \doteq 1.297 \qquad \bar{r} = \frac{3b}{1 - a^3}$$

$$\text{Variance} = \frac{72}{64} \qquad V(r) = \frac{72}{37} \qquad V(r) = \frac{3b + 3(3 - 1)b^2}{1 - a^3}$$

$$- \left(\frac{48}{64}\right)^2 = .5625 \qquad - \left(\frac{48}{37}\right)^2 = .2630 \qquad - \left(\frac{3b}{1 - a^3}\right)^2$$

know the "standard" results:

$$\bar{r} = sb \qquad V(r) = sab \qquad V(b') = \frac{ab}{s}$$

In our numerical example (i), $s = 3$ and $b = \frac{1}{4}$. Thus,

$$\bar{r} = 3 \times \frac{1}{4} = .75$$

and $V(r) = 3 \times \frac{3}{4} \times \frac{1}{4} = .5625$, as may be verified by long-hand calculation. If we let $b' = r/s$ denote the *proportion* of recessives (in contradistinction to the *number* of recessives) in a sibship, then $V(b') = V(r)/s^2 = ab/s$. For brevity, we may drop the prime of b' later on when there is no danger of confusion with b. In fact, the average value of b' is $\bar{r}/s = sb/s = b$.

In Case (ii) where the $r = 0$ class is missing, the mean number of recessives per sibship naturally beccmes larger than when the $r = 0$ class is present. Our numerical example shows that $\bar{r}$ has increased from .75 to 1.297. Further, in the complete distribution (i), r varies from 0 to 3; but in the truncated distribution (ii), r varies from 1 to 3. Therefore, the variance of the latter, $V(r) = .2630$, is smaller than that of the former, $V(r) = .5625$. In brief, the effect of truncation is to increase the mean but decrease the variance of r. We also should notice that the values of Σfr and Σfr^2 remain the same whether the distribution is complete or truncated, because the 0 class contributes no recessives. The difference between the two cases is in the total number of families Σf.

Case (iii) is a slight generalization of Case (ii), substituting the general notation a and b for $\frac{3}{4}$ and $\frac{1}{4}$. The column f gives the proportional frequencies, which add up to $1 - a^3$. This procedure, as explained in Proportional Frequencies, has no effect on the mean or variance of the distribution. The expressions for $\bar{r}$ and $V(r)$ are given at the bottom of the distribution, paving the way for generalization to sibships of any size.

Now we are ready for the general case. For sibships of size s, we find that (by replacing 3 by s):

$$\Sigma f = 1 - a^s \qquad \Sigma fr = sb \qquad \Sigma fr^2 = sb + s(s-1)b^2 = sab + s^2b^2$$

Hence the general formulas for the mean and variance of r of a truncated binomial distribution are:

$$\bar{r} = \frac{sb}{1 - a^s}$$

$$V(r) = \frac{sab + s^2b^2}{1 - a^s} - \left(\frac{sb}{1 - a^s}\right)^2 = sab\left[\frac{1 - a^s - sba^{s-1}}{(1 - a^s)^2}\right] = sab[\theta]$$

It is to be recalled that this $\bar{r}$ is larger than the standard sb and this $V(r)$ is smaller than the standard sab. The quantity $1 - a^s - sba^{s-1}$ is unity minus the first two terms of the binomial expansion. It may be shown quite easily that $(1 - a^s)^2$ is always larger than $(1 - a^s - sba^{s-1})$, so the expression in brackets, denoted by θ for brevity, is always smaller than unity. We may regard this fraction (θ) as the correction factor for variance of r without the 0 class.

Since $\bar{r} = sb/(1 - a^s)$ is the expected number of recessives per sibship of size s, the expected total number of recessives from all the sibships in the data is $\Sigma n_s \bar{r}_s$. If the observed total number of recessives is R, the equation $\Sigma n_s \bar{r}_s = R$ will give us an unbiased estimate of b. This is what we did in our numerical example (Table 5-3). Incidently, this is the estimate of b given by the method of maximum likelihood, a method that will not be developed in this book.

Variance of Estimated Proportion

In a complete binomial distribution, the proportion and number of recessives in a sibship are related by the simple expression $b = r/s$, or $r = sb$. On a per-sibship basis (i.e., regarding one sibship as one observation), the relationship becomes $r = sb/(1 - a^s)$ for a truncated binomial. Through the latter relationship we may find $V(b)$ from our knowledge of $V(r)$ by the "delta" method. Thus, differentiating, we find:

$$\frac{dr}{db} = \frac{s(1 - a^s - sba^{s-1})}{(1 - a^s)^2} = s\theta$$

$$V(r) = \left(\frac{dr}{db}\right)^2 V(b) = s^2\theta^2 V(b)$$

$$V(b) = \frac{V(r)}{s^2\theta^2} = \frac{sab\theta}{s^2\theta^2} = \frac{ab}{s}\left[\frac{1}{\theta}\right]$$

It is clear that for a truncated binomial, $V(b)$ is larger than the standard ab/s. It is a pleasant fact that $V(b)$ is enlarged to the same extent as $V(r)$ is decreased through truncation.

To combine the estimates of b from various sibships, each estimate should be weighted by the reciprocal of the variance. Hence the weight for an estimate of b from one sibship of size s is:

$$w_s = \frac{1}{V(b)_s} = \frac{s}{ab}[\theta] = \frac{s}{ab}\left[\frac{1 - a^s - sba^{s-1}}{(1 - a^s)^2}\right]$$

This is the value given in Table 5-2B. The total weight of the combined estimate of b from all the sibships is $W = \Sigma n_s w_s$, as calculated in our numerical example. Then the variance of the combined estimate of b is $1/W$.

Now, a few words about Tables 5-2A and B. They are calculated independently by the author, and they are s times the values tabulated by Lejeune (1958). The recalculation is to ensure the accuracy of the third decimal place. The values of Table 5-2B have also been tabulated by Finney (1949), except those for $b = .225$ and $b = .275$.

Historical Note

The two methods of correction, one for complete ascertainment and one for single ascertainment, were both originally devised by Weinberg (1912 and 1927). Discussions and applications of these methods are by Apert (1914), Just (1920), Bernstein (1929), Lenz (1929), and Hogben (1931). Major advances were made by Haldane (1932 and 1938) and Fisher (1934). Further elaborations were made by Finney (1949), Bailey (1951), Smith (1956, 1959), Lejeune (1958), and Morton (1959). Only a few of these papers are given in the References. Li (1954) and Steinberg (1959) are reviews.

Chapter 6

Association and Relative Risk

This chapter, in essence, gives a collection of statistical notes about association between two traits as determined by contingency tables and does not deal primarily with any specific genetic problem. The methods described here are applicable to genetic as well as to nongenetic traits. We shall use, whenever possible, genetic traits as examples because of their inherent interest to geneticists; but to illustrate a point, we shall not hesitate to employ hypothetical (and exaggerated) data. To grasp the fundamental principles is far more important than accumulating empirical "facts," which may turn out to be not so much facts as artifacts created by inappropriate statistical procedures. These notes are intended to call the reader's attention to certain aspects of the association problem and are not intended to take the place of a statistical textbook.

The Fourfold Table and Chi Square

It is best to begin with something that is presumed to be familiar to every reader. Let us consider the following fourfold (2 × 2) table, in which the symbol (1) denotes the presence of a certain trait or disease (arthritis, say) and the symbol (0) denotes its absence or the normal state.

The fourfold table arises in two different forms. First, the two rows are two separate samples of sizes n_1 and n_2. In this case we may wish to compare the two proportions (for arthritis) and test the significance of $(p_1 - p_2)$. Alternatively, the two rows may represent the classification of another trait of the same person.

Thus, "Sample 1" may stand for Rh-positive and "Sample 2" for Rh-negative individuals. In such a case we may wish to know if there is any association between the Rh type and arthritis. The physical setup and meaning are quite different in these two cases.

| | General Notation | | | | Numerical | Example | | |
	(1)	(0)	Total	Proportion	(1)	(0)	n_i	p_i
Sample 1	a_1	b_1	n_1	$p_1 = a_1/n_1$	66	54	120	.55
Sample 2	a_2	b_2	n_2	$p_2 = a_2/n_2$	54	126	180	.30
Total	A	B	N	$P = A/N$	120	180	300	.40

Undoubtedly most readers have learned the two statistical tests corresponding to the two situations separately. The immediate purpose in this section is to show that the procedures of testing the significance of $(p_1 - p_2)$ and of testing the independence of two traits are mathematically equivalent.

Each individual may either have arthritis (1) or not have it (0). The variance of each observation is the binomial variance, $PQ = (.4)(.6) = .24$. The variance of the mean (p_1) of the n_1 such individuals of Sample 1 is therefore PQ/n_1, and that for Sample 2 is PQ/n_2. By the usual procedure of testing the significance of the difference between two sample means, we obtain the *normal* deviate:

$$u = \frac{p_1 - p_2}{PQ\left(\frac{1}{n_1} + \frac{1}{n_2}\right)} = \frac{.55 - .30}{.24\left(\frac{1}{120} + \frac{1}{180}\right)} = 4.33$$

At the 0.05 significance level, u must exceed 1.96 to gain significance; and at the 0.01 level, u must exceed 2.5758 from the normal table. So the present result $(u = 4.33)$ is highly significant.

With one single degree of freedom, the square of the normal deviate is chi square. (This is the definition of chi square for one degree of freedom.) Thus, upon substitution of $N = n_1 + n_2$ and rearrangement,

$$u^2 = \chi^2 = \frac{n_1 n_2 (p_1 - p_2)^2}{NPQ} = \frac{120 \times 180(.55 - .30)^2}{300(.4)(.6)}$$

$$= 18.75 = (4.33)^2$$

From the chi-square table, we see that at the 0.05 significance level χ^2 with one degree of freedom must exceed $(1.96)^2 = 3.841$, and at the 0.01 level it must exceed $(2.5758)^2 = 6.635$ to gain significance.

On the other hand, if columns (1) and (0) represent the classification with respect to arthritis and the rows the classification of Rh type of the same individuals, we may calculate chi square to test the independence of the two attributes. The usual way to do this is first to calculate the "expected" numbers based on the marginal totals. For instance, the expected number corresponding to the cell occupied by a_1 is:

$$a_1' = \frac{A \times n_1}{N}, \text{ etc.}$$

Because the marginal totals are fixed numbers, the other three expected numbers can be obtained by subtraction. Then we take the deviations dev $= a_1 - a_1'$, etc. The deviations for the four cells are all equal in numerical value in this case. The chi-square value for the 2×2 table is then:

$$\chi^2 = \sum \frac{(\text{dev})^2}{\text{exp. no.}} = (\text{dev})^2 \left(\frac{1}{a_1'} + \frac{1}{b_1'} + \frac{1}{a_2'} + \frac{1}{b_2'} \right)$$

which, upon substitution and simplification, reduces to the all too familiar expression:

$$\chi^2 = \frac{(a_1 b_2 - a_2 b_1)^2 N}{ABn_1 n_2} = \frac{(66 \times 126 - 54 \times 54)^2 300}{120 \times 180 \times 120 \times 180} = 18.75$$

The two different-looking expressions for χ^2, one in terms of $(p_1 - p_2)$ and one in terms of $(a_1 b_2 - a_2 b_1)$, are mathematically identical, as may be readily verified by substituting $a_1 = n_1 p_1$, etc. Hence, the testing of independence is equivalent to testing the equality of two proportions.

Sample Size and Correlation

The chi square as calculated from a 2×2 table is directly proportional to the size of the sample for a given difference between the two p's. What we mean by this statement may be made clear by an example. Multiplying the observed numbers of the fourfold table in the previous section by a constant k (any fixed number, e.g., 2, 3, and $k = \frac{1}{6}$ in our numerical example for easy arithmetic), we obtain the following picture:

	(1)	(0)	Total	Proportion	(1)	(0)	n_i	p_i
Sample 1	ka_1	kb_1	kn_1	$p_1 = a_1/n_1$	11	9	20	.55
Sample 2	ka_2	kb_2	kn_2	$p_2 = a_2/n_2$	9	21	30	.30
Total	kA	kB	kN	$P = A/N$	20	30	50	.40

The relative magnitudes of the four observed numbers remain the same as before and thus the proportions p_i also remain the same. But the chi-square value for this table is k times that of the original table. Using either of the two expressions for χ^2 given previously, or calculating the χ^2 from the new numerical table, we see immediately that:

$$\text{new } \chi^2 = k\chi^2 = \frac{1}{6} \times 18.75 = 3.125$$

Similarly, if we had doubled each of the observed numbers of the original table, the new chi square would be

$$2\chi^2 = 2 \times 18.75 = 37.50$$

It will be noted that when $p_1 = .55$ and $p_2 = .30$, the sample sizes $n_1 = 20$ and $n_2 = 30$ yield a $\chi^2 = 3.125$, smaller than that required for significance. For the same p_i values, the larger samples ($n_1 = 120$ and $n_2 = 180$) show a highly significant difference. The chi-square value clearly depends on the difference between two proportions as well as on the absolute size of the samples. For samples of a given size, the larger the difference between the p's, the larger the chi square. For samples of a given difference, the larger the samples, the larger the chi square. For a small difference, the chi square may be made very large by increasing the sample size. Therefore, the chi square is useful in detecting association or difference in proportions, but it is not in itself a measure of the degree of association.

The product-moment correlation coefficient, r, provides a measure of the degree of association independent of the sample size. To calculate the value of r, we must first assign some numerical values to the attributes concerned. Adopting the binomial system again, we assign the value 1 to those with arthritis and 0 to those without. For the other attribute, we take the Rh-positive individuals as having the value (1) and Rh-negative persons as (0). (It makes no difference to the correlation coefficient if we adopt any other sets of arbitrary values.) With such numerical values assigned, the 2×2 table may be regarded as a small correlation table, from which the correlation coefficient may be calculated in the usual manner. This yields:

$$r = \frac{N(a_1 - a_1')}{\sqrt{ABn_1n_2}} = \frac{a_1b_2 - a_2b_1}{\sqrt{ABn_1n_2}} = \sqrt{\frac{n_1n_2}{AB}} \cdot (p_1 - p_2)$$

In our numerical example, the reader will readily find that $r = 0.25$ for both the table with $N = 300$ and the table with $N = 50$. In fact, if we divide every number of the latter table by 50 so the grand total of the new table becomes unity, the correlation coefficient remains $r = .25$. From the algebraic expressions for r, we see immediately that:

$$Nr^2 = \chi^2 \qquad r^2 = \frac{\chi^2}{N} \qquad r = \sqrt{\frac{\chi^2}{N}}$$

Thus, in our numerical case, we have $300(.25)^2 = 18.75$ for the first table and $50(.25)^2 = 3.125$ for the second table.

It should also be noted that if the two attributes have the same variance $(AB = n_1n_2)$, the correlation coefficient is simply $r = p_1 - p_2$ and $\chi^2 = N(p_1 - p_2)^2$; the normal deviate is then $u = \sqrt{N} \cdot (p_1 - p_2) = r\sqrt{N}$. In genetic problems, especially those dealing with relatives, the two marginal distributions often have the same mean and the same variance, and it will be handy to know these simple relationships.

Association and Incidence

Once more, let (1) denote the presence of arthritis and (0) its absence. We wish to study whether there is any association between the husband's condition and that of his wife with respect to arthritis. If the anomaly is due to some common adult environmental factors (e.g., food of the family or humidity of the residence), it is reasonable to expect some association between husband and wife. Suppose that the findings about the husband-wife pairs are as follows:

		Husband (1)	Husband (0)			Husband (1)	Husband (0)			Husband (1)	Husband (0)	
Wife	(1)	1	9	10	(1)	16	24	40	(1)	49	21	70
	(0)	9	81	90	(0)	24	36	60	(0)	21	9	30
		10	90	100		40	60	100		70	30	100
		Ages 31–45				Ages 46–60				Ages 61–75		

It is seen that for each age group, there is no association between husband and wife. The reader should verify that for each 2×2 table, $\chi^2 = r = 0$. The conclusion is clear: there is no association for arthritis at any age. Some investigators would like to combine all the tables together to obtain a table with larger number of observations, thinking that the result based on the combined table would give us an over-all or average picture. If that is done, the following combined table is obtained:

		Husband (1)	Husband (0)	Total
Wife	(1)	66	54	120
	(0)	54	126	180
Total		120	180	300

for which $\chi^2 = 18.75$ and $r = 0.25$, indicating a highly significant association between husband and wife with respect to arthritis condition. This result may disturb him. What is wrong? Should he believe the separate small tables or the combined big table?

We note that the incidence of arthritis for young couples is 10 per cent, for the middle-aged, 40 per cent; and for the old, 70 per cent. (The marginal incidences need not be the same for husbands and wives; they are equal in our numerical example for arithmetic simplicity. The reader may construct more complicated examples as exercises.) The older we are, the more likely we are to get arthritis. When the incidence of a trait increases or decreases with age, the combined table for all ages will yield a false association, an artifact entirely due to the changing incidence for the various age groups. This principle applies not only to age but to any other criterion by which the separate tables are constructed. The point to be firmly remembered is that apparent association may be created through intermixture; it is due to the heterogeneity (in incidence) of the materials rather than to any inherent association. We use age as an example here because it is easy to visualize the situation and because it is all too common a practice to combine tables of all ages without first carefully studying the possible change in incidence for the various age groups.

Now, let us examine another type of statement. "Ninety per cent of the time both husband and wife have arthritis." It seems to hint that there is strong correlation between husband and wife. Actually, this statement by itself tells us nothing at all about association. For, if the incidence of arthritis among husbands is 96 per cent and that among wives is 94 per cent, then the expected (on the basis of no association) frequency of arthritis in husband-wife pairs is $(.96)(.94) = .90$. This brings out the point that association cannot be described by the frequency of concordant events alone. The marginal incidence must be stated. In other words, association can be exhibited properly only by a two-way table and not by any single number in a cell. In mathematical language, the association is determined not by the probability p_{ij} but by its comparison with the product $p_i p_j$.

We have dealt with association due to intermixture when both marginal incidences increase with age. In another and probably less common situation, in which the incidence of one attribute increases while that of the other decreases with age (or any other group criterion), the effect of combining tables is the reverse. The effect may be made clear by examining the following two rows of tables:

Group I			Group II			Combined		
6	4	10	14	26	40	20	30	50
44	46	90	16	44	60	60	90	150
50	50	100	30	70	100	80	120	200

Group I			Group II			Combined		
5	5	10	12	28	40	17	33	50
45	45	90	18	42	60	63	87	150
50	50	100	30	70	100	80	120	200

In the first row, both Group I and Group II exhibit some degree of positive association; yet in the combined table there is none. In the second row, both Group I and Group II show independence, but the combined table shows negative association. The conclusion is that when the marginal incidences change in opposite directions, the combined table will decrease (algebraically) the degree of association, changing positive to zero and changing zero to negative.

In view of these illustrations, it is clear that one must exercise caution in pooling tables together to obtain an over-all picture. The picture so obtained may be quite out of focus.

Quantitative Traits

What has been said of the false association between two attributes due to pooling of heterogeneous groups may be seen even more easily for measurement data when expressed in the form of a scatter diagram (Fig. 6-1). In Group I (dots) there is no correlation between the measurements x and y; neither is there any in Group II (circles). If both x and y are higher in Group II than in Group I, the combined data will show a positive correlation (Fig. 6-1A). If one variable is larger and the other smaller in one group than in the other, the combined data will show a negative correlation (Fig. 6-1B). The situation is analogous to the pooling of contingency tables of attributes with different incidences. True

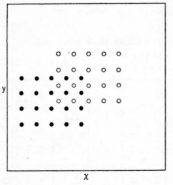 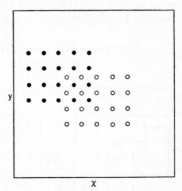

A. Artifactitious positive correlation   **B. Artifactitious negative correlation**

FIG. 6-1. Correlation due to intermixture. *A*, artifactitious positive correlation. *B*, artifactitious negative correlation.

association or correlation must be studied within a homogeneous group.

Components of Correlation

When the marginal distributions of x and y in one group have the same mean and variance as those in another group, these two groups may be combined to yield an average correlation. For illustration, Table 6-1 gives three separate groups with the same marginal distributions. In Group I, the correlation coefficient is $r = {}^{72}\!/_{88}$; in Group II, $r = {}^{52}\!/_{88}$. For the combined data I + II, the correlation is $\frac{1}{2}(72 + 52)/88 = {}^{62}\!/_{88}$. As long as the marginal distributions have the same mean and variance, any number of tables may be combined to yield an average correlation. Thus, for the combination (I + II) + (II + III) = I + 2II + III, the correlation is:

$$r = \tfrac{1}{4}\left(\frac{72}{88}\right) + \tfrac{1}{2}\left(\frac{52}{88}\right) + \tfrac{1}{4}\left(\frac{12}{88}\right) = \frac{47}{88}$$

The three terms that make up the correlation $^{47}\!/_{88}$ represent the contributions of the three separate groups and may be regarded as components of the total correlation. If the various groups are of different sizes the weight employed in averaging the correlation should be proportional to the size of the group.

TABLE 6-1. CORRELATION TABLES IN WHICH THE
MARGINAL DISTRIBUTIONS HAVE THE
SAME MEAN AND VARIANCE

I

2				2
	1	1		2
	1	2	3	6
2	2	3	3	10

$$r = \frac{72}{88}$$

II

1		1		2
1	1			2
	1	2	3	6
2	2	3	3	10

$$r = \frac{52}{88}$$

III

1			1	2
		1	1	2
1	1	2	2	6
2	2	3	3	10

$$r = \frac{12}{88}$$

I + II

3		1		4
1	2	1		4
	2	4	6	12
4	4	6	6	20

$$r = \frac{62}{88}$$

II + III

2		1	1	4
1	2	1		4
1	2	4	5	12
4	4	6	6	20

$$r = \frac{32}{88}$$

I + 2II + III

5		2	1	8
2	4	2		8
1	4	8	11	24
8	8	12	12	40

$$r = \frac{47}{88}$$

Just as separate tables can be combined, a composite table can be decomposed into separate component parts. In calculating the correlation between full sibs (Chap. 12), we shall make use of this simple property of correlation. Needless to say, when the corresponding marginal distributions of the separate groups do not have the same mean and variance, such groups cannot be combined as they are.

However, when the variables are standardized (all with zero mean and unit variance), the correlation coefficient is the standardized covariance, which can then be combined or separated in much the same way as the variance. A whole set of statistical techniques, known as the *method of path coefficients*, has been developed by Sewall Wright, in 1917–1921, on the basis of standardized variables and the additive property of correlation. A discussion of these techniques is outside the scope of this book. Interested readers may consult the review by Li (1956a).

Relative Risk

The chi square and correlation coefficient are statistical entities with known sampling distributions that enable us to make certain probability statements. Beyond that, they have no concrete physical meaning. In certain types of research, such as that concerning the association of blood group with peptic ulcer or diabetes mellitus, the trend is to develop an index that has a simple and direct physical meaning; hence the concept of *relative risk*.

In the study of man, there are in general two types of approach —the *prospective* (forward) and the *retrospective* (backward). To sharpen the difference between the two, the following setup and notations are introduced:

	Prospective Study		*Retrospective Study*	
			Diseased propositi	*Control population*
	Disease	*Normal*		
Given A	$P(dis \mid A)$	$P(nor \mid A)$	A $P(A \mid dis)$	$P(A)$
Given O	$P(dis \mid O)$	$P(nor \mid O)$	O $P(O \mid dis)$	$P(O)$

The symbol *dis* denotes the presence of the disease (ulcer, diabetes, etc.) and *nor* the absence of it. These symbols are more descriptive and easier to remember than D and $\bar{D}$ (which may be employed by more experienced readers). A and O, as usual, denote the blood groups. For the time being, we may suppose either that there are only two blood groups in the population or that A represents the combined A + AB groups and O represents the combined O + B groups or some other combinations. This point will be discussed below under Partition of Total Chi Square.

The expression $P(dis \mid A)$ stands for the *conditional* probability of having the disease given that the individual is of blood group A, or, briefly, the probability of disease given A. Similarly, $P(A \mid dis)$ is the probability that the individual belongs to group A given that he has the disease. The symbol $P(A)$ is simply the probability that an individual belongs to group A in the general or control population, disease or no disease. With the symbols so defined, the probabilities in each box add to unity; thus,

$$P(dis \mid A) + P(nor \mid A) = 1$$
$$P(A) + P(O) = 1, \text{ etc.}$$

It is seen that the direct information obtained by forward and by backward studies is quite different. In a prospective study to determine whether group A individuals have a greater probability of contracting the disease than group O individuals, the information on $P(A)$ and $P(O)$ of the general population is really not necessary. The relative risk of contracting the disease for group A to group O individuals is defined as the ratio:

$$x = \frac{P(dis \mid A)}{P(dis \mid O)}$$

Both $P(dis \mid A)$ and $P(dis \mid O)$ are directly determined by a prospective study, and the ratio x may be calculated at once. For example, if we regard the first table under The Fourfold Table and Chi Square (p. 80) as results of a *prospective* study and let sample 1 consist of A individuals and sample 2 of O individuals, we have $P(dis \mid A) = .55$ and $P(dis \mid O) = .30$ and $x = .55/.30 = 1.83$. This means that group A individuals have a probability 83 per cent higher than that for group O individuals in contracting the disease.

Unfortunately, prospective studies in man are not always possible or practical, especially with rare diseases and those with late onset. So most investigators resort to retrospective studies, obtaining a group of propositi with the disease to begin with and comparing the proportions of A and O in the propositi group with those in the general population. The question is: Can this type of study furnish any information on the meaningful ratio $x = P(dis \mid A)/P(dis \mid O)$? The answer is yes; the value of the ratio x can be obtained from a backward study, although neither $P(dis \mid A)$ nor $P(dis \mid O)$ is known separately. A proof of this assertion is in order.

Let $P(dis)$ be the probability of contracting the disease in the general population and $P(A, dis)$ be the probability that an individual belongs to group A *and* has the disease. By elementary theory of probability we have (Levene, 1956):

$$P(A, dis) = P(A) \, P(dis \mid A) = P(dis) \, P(A \mid dis)$$
$$P(O, dis) = P(O) \, P(dis \mid O) = P(dis) \, P(O \mid dis)$$

Dividing the first expression by the second, canceling and rearranging, we obtain:

$$x = \frac{P(dis \mid A)}{P(dis \mid O)} = \frac{P(A \mid dis)}{P(O \mid dis)} \cdot \frac{P(O)}{P(A)}$$

The four probabilities on the right-hand side are exactly those obtained from a retrospective study. To illustrate, let us consider the following hypothetical results of a backward study of the association between blood group and diabetes among white males.

	Diseased Propositi Number	Proportion	Control Population Number	Proportion
A	$h = 106$	0.530	$H = 1,800$	0.450
O	$k = 94$	0.470	$K = 2,200$	0.550
Total	$n = 200$	1.000	$N = 4,000$	1.000

According to the formula above, the ratio of the risk of diabetes among A individuals to that among O individuals is:

$$x = \frac{0.530}{0.470} \cdot \frac{0.550}{0.450} = 1.378$$

Or, more directly, in terms of observed numbers,

$$x = \frac{106}{94} \cdot \frac{2200}{1800} = 1.378$$

On the face of these data, males of type A have a 37.8 per cent greater risk of developing diabetes than do males of type O.

Sampling Variance

Let h,k be the observed numbers in the diseased propositi and H,K be the corresponding numbers in the control group. Then we have:

$$V(h) = V(k) = \frac{hk}{n} \qquad Cov(h,k) = \frac{-hk}{n}$$

The expressions for H and K are similar. The covariance for h (or k) and H (or K) is zero, since they belong to two separate samples. The relative risk is estimated by:

$$x = \frac{h}{k} \cdot \frac{K}{H}$$

The sampling variance of x is quite involved. However, a logarithmic transformation renders the problem exceedingly simple. Thus, taking the natural log,

$$y = \log x = (\log h - \log k) + (\log K - \log H)$$

Denoting $(\log h - \log k)$ by y', we need only work out $V(y')$.

$$dy' = \frac{dh}{h} - \frac{dk}{k}$$

$$V(y') = \frac{V(h)}{h^2} + \frac{V(k)}{k^2} - \frac{2 \, cov(h,k)}{hk}$$

Substituting,

$$V(y') = \frac{hk}{h^2 n} + \frac{hk}{k^2 n} + \frac{2hk}{hkn}$$

$$= \frac{(h + k)^2}{(h + k)hk} = \frac{1}{h} + \frac{1}{k}$$

Hence (Wilson, 1951; Woolf, 1955),

$$V(y) = \frac{1}{h} + \frac{1}{k} + \frac{1}{H} + \frac{1}{K}$$

In our numerical example, $y = \log_e x = \log_e 1.378 = 0.3206$

$$V(y) = \frac{1}{106} + \frac{1}{94} + \frac{1}{1,800} + \frac{1}{2,200} = .02108 \qquad s(y) = .1452$$

If there is no difference in the probability of developing diabetes among the A and O individuals, the expected value of x is unity and that of y is zero. The normal deviation

$$u = \frac{y}{s(y)} = \frac{.3206}{.1452} = 2.208$$

is significant at the .05 level. Alternatively, we may calculate the chi square with one degree of freedom:

$$\chi^2 = u^2 = \frac{y^2}{V(y)} = \frac{.10278}{.02108} = 4.876$$

The estimate $x = hK/kH$ is biased, as is usually the case with the estimate of ratios. For small samples, the bias is not always negligible. Haldane (1956) shows that if we add $\frac{1}{2}$ to each of the four observed numbers and then take the ratio, the estimate will have a much smaller bias. The improved estimate is:

$$x = \frac{h + \frac{1}{2}}{k + \frac{1}{2}} \cdot \frac{K + \frac{1}{2}}{H + \frac{1}{2}} = \frac{2h + 1}{2k + 1} \cdot \frac{2K + 1}{2H + 1}$$

As before $y = \log_e x$. The variance of the improved y is smaller:

$$V(y) = \frac{1}{h + 1} + \frac{1}{k + 1} + \frac{1}{H + 1} + \frac{1}{K + 1}$$

In our numerical example, the improved values are $x = 1.377$, $y = .3200$, $V(y) = .02088$, and $\chi^2 = 4.90$. These refinements make very little difference for large samples, but they should be used whenever the observed numbers are small (say, below 50).

Combined Estimate and Heterogeneity

For each set of data (h, k, H, K), the values of x, y, $V(y)$, and χ^2 are calculated as in the preceding sections. To obtain a combined (or average) estimate of y from several sets of data, each y should be weighted by the reciprocal of its variance, viz., $w = 1/V(y)$.

Then the combined estimate ($\bar{y}$) and its variance are:

$$\bar{y} = \frac{\Sigma wy}{\Sigma w} \qquad V(\bar{y}) = \frac{1}{\Sigma w}$$

The antilogarithm of $\bar{y}$ is taken as the combined estimate of the ratio x. The significance of the combined estimate $\bar{y}$ is tested by:

$$\chi^2 = \frac{\bar{y}^2}{V(\bar{y})} = \frac{(\Sigma wy)^2}{\Sigma w} = \bar{y}^2 \Sigma w$$

Table 6-2 gives a numerical example of combining three sets of similar data. Since the group O individuals have a greater risk of developing peptic ulcer, we here use h and H to denote the observed numbers of the group O individuals. (In the previous example, it is group A that has a greater risk of developing diabetes.) Thus, for the London data, $x = 911 \times 4219/579 \times 4578 = 1.4500$, and $V(y) = 1/911 + \cdots = 0.003280$, the reciprocal of which is the weight $w = 304.9$. The chi square for each city is $\chi^2 = y^2/V(y) = wy^2$.

TABLE 6-2. COMBINED ESTIMATE OF RELATIVE RISK OF PEPTIC ULCER
IN GROUPS O AND A (AIRD et al., 1954; WOOLF, 1955)

City	Blood group	Peptic ulcer	Control population	$x = \dfrac{hK}{kH}$	$y = \log_e x$	$w = \dfrac{1}{V(y)}$	$\chi^2 = wy^2$
London	O	911	4,578	1.4500	0.3716	304.9	42.11
	A	579	4,219				
Manchester	O	361	4,532	1.2224	0.2008	136.6	5.50
	A	246	3,775				
New Castle	O	396	6,598	1.4418	0.3659	134.5	18.01
	A	219	5,261				
Total	...	...	.....	......	$\Sigma wy = 189.94$	$\Sigma w = 576.0$	65.62

The sum of three separate chi squares for the three cities is 65.62 with three degrees of freedom. The combined estimate from the three cities is $\bar{y} = 189.94/576.0 = 0.3298$, and

$$V(\bar{y}) = \frac{1}{576} = .001736$$

and s.d.$_{\bar{y}}$ = .041665. The 95 per cent confidence interval of $\bar{y}$ is:

$$\bar{y} \pm 1.96(.041665)$$

The chi square attributed to the combined estimate is:

$$\chi^2 = \frac{(189.94)^2}{576} = (.3298)^2\, 576 = 62.63$$

If the three sets of data have identical proportions, this χ^2 should be equal to the sum of the three separate chi squares of the cities. Thus, by subtraction, we obtain the chi square due to heterogeneity of the three sets of data as follows:

Source	Degrees of freedom	χ^2
Combined estimate $\bar{y}$	1	$62.63 = \bar{y}^2 \Sigma w$
Heterogeneity	2	$2.99 = \Sigma w y^2 - \bar{y}^2 \Sigma w$
Total (three cities)	3	$65.62 = \Sigma w y^2$

It is seen that it is justified to have the three sets of data combined, because of the small heterogeneity.

Finally, the combined estimate of the relative risk is $\bar{x}$ = antilog $\bar{y}$ = antilog .3298 = 1.39, indicating that the O individuals have a 39 per cent greater risk of developing peptic ulcer than the A individuals, and the difference is significant. It should be noted that, if the three sets of observed numbers are first added together and then the incidence ratio is calculated, it will be found that X = 1.35 and it is not equal to the $\bar{x}$ converted from $\bar{y}$.

Partition of Total Chi Square

We have been dealing with the comparison of two rates so far. When the observed numbers of all four blood types are large, perhaps we should look into the relative risk of all four groups. If we must pool the four groups into two, how shall we do it? One way of investigating this problem is to subdivide the total chi square into components with a single degree of freedom and see which contrast accounts for the largest portion of variation. As an exam-

TABLE 6-3. TOTAL CHI SQUARE WITH THREE DEGREES OF FREEDOM
AND ITS SUBDIVISION INTO COMPONENTS WITH SINGLE DEGREE
OF FREEDOM

Blood type	Ulcer patients a_i	Controls b_i	Total n_i	$p_i = a_i/n_i$	$p_i a_i = a_i^2/n_i$
AB	43	226	269	0.15985	6.8736
B	134	570	704	.19034	25.5057
A	679	2625	3304	.20551	139.5403
O	983	2892	3875	.25368	249.3649

Total	1839	6313	8152	$P = .22559$	$\Sigma p_i a_i = 421.2845$
				$Q = .77441$	$P\Sigma a_i = 414.8578$
				$PQ = .17470$	diff. $= 6.4267$

$$\chi^2 = \frac{\Sigma p_i a_i - P\Sigma a_i}{PQ} = \frac{6.4267}{0.1747} = 36.787$$

Blood type	Subdivision I		Crude χ^2	Adjustment	Adjusted χ^2
AB	43	226	1.216	$\dfrac{.1488}{.1747}$	1.036
B	134	570			
A	679	2625	23.258	$\dfrac{.1779}{.1747}$	23.686
O	983	2892			
AB + B	177	796	12.065	1.00	12.065
A + O	1662	5517			
					Total 36.787

Blood type	Subdivision II		Crude χ^2	Adjustment	Adjusted χ^2
AB	43	226	1.216	$\dfrac{.1488}{.1747}$	1.306
B	134	570			
AB + B	177	796	2.614	$\dfrac{.1601}{.1747}$	2.396
A	679	2625			
AB + A + B	856	3421	33.355	1.00	33.355
O	983	2892			
					Total 36.787

ple, the data of an Iowa study on ABO–peptic ulcer association (Buckwalter et al., 1956) are reproduced in Table 6-3, the upper portion of which gives the total chi square with three degrees of freedom and the lower portion gives two different orthogonal subdivisions, each yielding three single components. The arithmetic for calculating the total χ^2 is given in some detail, not only because it is the most expedient numerical procedure, but also because the p_i values indicate how the four groups vary. The total $\chi^2 = 36.787$ with three degrees of freedom is highly significant.

The method of subdivision may need a few words of explanation. Let us consider the subdivision system I. From the original 2×4 table we construct three separate 2×2 tables as indicated, and for each of them the ordinary χ^2 is calculated in the usual manner. These are designated as the *crude* χ^2 in the table. The total χ^2 is in units of the variance $PQ = .1747$, but the χ^2 for the first 2×2 table, for instance, is in units of pq, where p is the average proportion of that table alone and is equal to $(43 + 134)/\text{table total} = {}^{177}\!/_{973} = .1819$; hence

$$pq = .1819 \times .8181 = .1488$$

Multiplying the crude χ^2 by the adjusting factor pq/PQ, we obtain the *adjusted* χ^2. In subdivision system I, we see that the mere comparison of A and O accounts for only $23.686/36.787 = 64$ per cent of the total χ^2. The comparison $(AB + B)$ versus $(A + O)$ is also significant. Alternatively, we may compare AB versus A, B versus O, and $(AB + A)$ versus $(B + O)$. The reader may do this as an exercise. The adjusted χ^2 are, respectively, 2.968, 13.680, 20.139, totaling 36.787. This subdivision is apparently not satisfactory either.

In subdivision system II, the three separate 2×2 tables are constructed cumulatively: first AB versus B, then $(AB + B)$ versus A, and finally $(AB + A + B)$ versus O. The calculation of the adjusted χ^2 follows the same procedure. Here we see that the last comparison accounts for more than 90 per cent of the total χ^2, and the other two components are nonsignificant. It is clear that almost all the variation is due to the difference between type O and the others. It follows that if we must pool the four blood types into two, it should be O versus non-O.

If we wish, the relative risk of AB, B, and A to O individuals can be investigated separately, using the O individuals as the standard. Table 6-4 gives the results of such comparisons, based

TABLE 6-4. ESTIMATION OF RELATIVE RISK AND
ITS CONFIDENCE INTERVAL

Comparison	Relative risk, x	$y = \log_e x$	$s.d._y$	Confidence interval of x
O versus AB	1.786	0.5800	.1704	1.279–2.495
O versus B	1.446	.3688	.1029	1.182–1.769
O versus A	1.314	.2731	.0567	1.176–1.469
O versus others	1.358	.3060	.0531	1.224–1.507

on the data of Table 6-3. If we let the risk of developing ulcer for O individuals be 100 per so many individuals, then the relative risks of the other blood types are as follows:

$$
\begin{array}{ccccccc}
AB & : & B & : & A & : & O \\
1/1.786 & : & 1/1.446 & : & 1/1.314 & : & 1 \\
56 & : & 69 & : & 76 & : & 100
\end{array}
$$

It seems that AB individuals have the least risk of ulceration. For intrafamily studies, see Clarke (1959).

The True Rates

In the previous sections we have been dealing with the ratio of two "true rates" for a certain disease, without knowing either of them separately. This is due to the retrospective nature of the study, in which we employed the general population as the control group; thus the notations $P(A)$ and $P(O)$ in our previous setup. But not all retrospective studies employ a section of the general population as control. Sometimes, investigators purposely select a contrasting group as control in retrospective studies. The study on the possible association between cigarette smoking and lung cancer provides a good example, which we shall use for illustration. The association between smoking and cancer is not primarily a genetic problem, although some prominent geneticists both in this country and in Great Britain are deeply involved in it. Our discussion here, however, will be limited to the single purpose of showing how the true disease rates can also be estimated from a retrospective study.

In reading the following, blood groups A and O should be identified with smokers and nonsmokers, and lung cancer with the disease (diabetes, ulcer, etc.). The true rates we are interested in are the *conditional* probabilities: $\mu_1 = P(\text{cancer} \mid \text{smoker})$ for the smokers; $\mu_2 = P(\text{cancer} \mid \text{nonsmoker})$ for the nonsmokers. In a retrospective study we start out with a group of lung cancer patients and a comparable group *without* lung cancer and determine the proportions of smokers in each group. The information so obtained estimates the conditional probabilities:

$$p_1 = P(\text{smoker} \mid \text{cancer}) \text{ in cancer group}$$
$$p_2 = P(\text{smoker} \mid \text{no cancer}) \text{ in control group}$$

If this information is supplemented by the extraneous knowledge about the incidence of lung cancer in the general population (smokers and nonsmokers), then the composition of the general population can be reconstructed and the true cancer rate estimated.

Let $X = P(\text{cancer})$ be the incidence of lung cancer in the general population. From the conditional probabilities p_1 and p_2, we infer that the composition of the general population must be as follows (Cornfield, 1951):

	With cancer	*Without cancer*	*Total*
Smokers	$p_1 X$	$p_2(1 - X)$	$p_2 + (p_1 - p_2)X$
Nonsmokers	$(1 - p_1)X$	$(1 - p_2)(1 - X)$	$1 - p_2 - (p_1 - p_2)X$
Total	X	$1 - X$	1.00

Hence, the true cancer rates for smokers and nonsmokers are, respectively,

$$\mu_1 = \frac{p_1 X}{p_2 + (p_1 - p_2)X} \qquad \mu_2 = \frac{(1 - p_1)X}{1 - p_2 - (p_1 - p_2)X}$$

If the cancer incidence X is small (say, of the order of 10^{-4} to 10^{-5}) in comparison with the smoking proportions p_1 and p_2, then the quantity $(p_1 - p_2)X$ in the denominator may be omitted. That is, approximately,

$$\mu_1 = \frac{p_1 X}{p_2} \qquad \mu_2 = \frac{(1 - p_1)X}{1 - p_2}$$

Sample estimates of μ_1 and μ_2 may be made according to these formulas. Let h and k be the observed numbers of smokers and nonsmokers in the cancer group of size $n = h + k$ and H, K, N be the corresponding numbers in the group *without* lung cancer. Estimates are then:

$$u_1 = \frac{h}{H} \frac{NX}{n} \qquad u_2 = \frac{k}{K} \frac{NX}{n}$$

The variance, again, takes a very simple form on logarithmic scale (Li, 1961):

$$V(y_1) = V(\log_e u_1) = \frac{1}{h} + \frac{1}{H} - \frac{1}{n} - \frac{1}{N}$$

$$V(y_2) = V(\log_e u_2) = \frac{1}{k} + \frac{1}{K} - \frac{1}{n} - \frac{1}{N}$$

from which the confidence interval of y_1 and y_2 may be constructed in the usual manner. Their antilogs are then taken as the corresponding limits of u_1 and u_2.

As an example, let us estimate the true cancer rate for smokers from the following data:

	Lung cancer group	Without lung cancer
Smokers:	$h = 27$	$H = 99$
Nonsmokers:	$k = 8$	$K = 72$
Total:	$n = 35$	$N = 171$

It is known from public health statistics that the incidence of lung cancer is $X = 15.5 \times 10^{-5}$ for the section of the general population from which the studies have been made. The estimate of μ_1 is then:

$$u_1 = \frac{h}{H} \frac{NX}{n} = \frac{27}{99} \cdot \frac{171}{35} \times 15.5 \times 10^{-5} = 20.6 \times 10^{-5}$$

$$y_1 = \log_e u_1 = \log_e 20.6 - 5 \log_e 10 = 3.02529 - 11.51293$$

$$V(y_1) = \frac{1}{27} + \frac{1}{99} - \frac{1}{35} - \frac{1}{171} = .012719 \qquad \text{s. e.} = .11278$$

Confidence limits of y_1 are $y_1 \mp 1.96(.11278) = 2.8042$ and 3.2463, each to be diminished by 11.5129. The corresponding limits of u_1 are their antilogs, viz., 16.5 and 25.7, each multiplied by 10^{-5}. Similar calculations can be made for u_2, which turns out to be 8.4×10^{-5}; their ratio is $20.6:8.4 = 2.45$.

When X is small, $P(\text{smoker})$ differs very little from $P(\text{smoker} \mid \text{no cancer})$. In estimating the ratio μ_1/μ_2, we arrive at the same result as before, i.e., $x = u_1/u_2 = hK/Hk = 2.45$, independent of X. It should be reiterated that this is true only when X is small.

Chapter 7

Simple Equilibrium Models

Some simple models of equilibrium are introduced in this chapter; their applications in genetics will be dealt with in the following two chapters. Whether it is due to greater familiarity with, and interest in, the material or to a psychological barrier, it is a fact that problems about money and cars are more readily understood than those about genes and chromosomes, although in some instances the mathematical nature of the problems is the same or almost the same in the two cases. Familiar analogies are used in this chapter because they give us a ready grasp of the principles involved. Those who have learned about genetic equilibrium in genetic context and can only express it in that technical language may not really see the basic mechanisms at work.

GAME OF GIVE AND TAKE

Rule of Exchange and Equilibrium

Mr. A has $20 and Mr. B has $280. The total amount between them is $300. They agree on a rule of exchanging their wealth. The rule is that Mr. A gives *one-half* of what he has to Mr. B, and at the same time Mr. B gives *one-quarter* of his wealth to Mr. A. Thus, Mr. A, having $20, gives $10 to Mr. B; and B, having $280, gives $70 to A. This completes one operation of exchange. The result is that A now has $80 and B has $220, as shown in Case I of Table 7-1. The total number of dollars remains 300, of course. The game of exchange continues according to the same rule. Now A, having $80, must give $40 to B, and B, having $220, must give

$55 to A. The result of this exchange is that A has $95 and B, $205. Continuation of the game strictly according to the rule will necessarily involve small changes (cents and mils), but for our present purpose we will be accurate only to the dollar. So in the next operation A gives $47 to B, and B gives $51 to A. After a few exchanges it is seen that A has $100 and B, $200. When this stage is reached, further exchange no longer alters the wealth of the two persons. Mr. A, having $100, gives half of it, or $50, to B; and B, having $200, gives one-quarter of it, or $50, to A. The amount of give and take exactly balances, so after the exchange A still has $100 and B still has $200. This situation is called the *equilibrium condition*. The fact that the wealth of A and B remains the same does not at all imply the termination of the game of give and take. The mutual exchange process still goes on, but it does not alter the relative wealth of the two persons any more.

Equilibrium Determined by Rule of Game

One may argue that Mr. A ended up with less money than Mr. B because he started out with less money. Well, to see if this is the reason, we start another game with the same rules, but this time we let Mr. A have more money than Mr. B in the beginning, as shown in Case II of Table 7-1. A gives $\frac{1}{2}(\$260) = \$130$ to B, and B gives $\frac{1}{4}(\$40) = \$10$ to A, in the first exchange. It is seen that, after a few exchanges, exactly the same equilibrium condition is reached, with A having $100 and B having $200. It is clear then that it is not the initial amount of money that determines the equilibrium condition.

Since the equilibrium condition means that the amount of income and outgo must balance each other, and since income and outgo depend on the rules of give and take, it follows that it is the rule of the game that determines the equilibrium condition. In other words, A's $100 and B's $200 are the consequences of the agreement that A gives 50 per cent of his assets to B and in return B gives 25 per cent of his to A. The reader may try any other initial conditions (e.g., A starts with $210 and B with $90) and convince himself that under the same rules the same equilibrium condition will be obtained. Mr. A will end up with one-third of the $300 and B with two-thirds.

The total amount $300 used in the example above is arbitrary and chosen for arithmetic convenience. A less arbitrary approach is to use percentages, whatever the total may be. An example of this type is shown in Case III of Table 7-1. Mr. A starts with 20

TABLE 7-1. GAME OF GIVE AND TAKE*

Case I		Case II		Case III	
Mr. A	Mr. B	Mr. A	Mr. B	Mr. A	Mr. B
20 →10 ←70	280	260 →130 ←10	40	.200 →.100 ←.200	.800
80 →40 ←55	220	140 →70 ←40	160	.300 →.150 ←.175	.700
95 →47 ←51	205	110 →55 ←47	190	.325 →.162 ←.169	.675
99 →49 ←50	201	102 →51 ←49	198	.332 →.166 ←.167	.668
100 →50 ←50	200	100 →50 ←50	200	.333 →.166 ←.167	.667
100 →50 ←50	200	100 →50 ←50	200	.333 →.167 ←.167	.667

* The rule is that Mr. A gives 50% of what he has to Mr. B; at the same time Mr. B gives 25% of what he has to Mr. A. The game continues until the exchange does not alter the wealth of either party.

per cent of the total money, and B has 80 per cent. After a few exchanges under the same rule of give and take, it is seen that A will have one-third and B two-thirds of the total.

The remaining question is: What is the precise relationship between the rule of give and take and the final equilibrium value? An examination of the numerical examples shows that Mr. A, who gives away a higher proportion of his property, has less money in the equilibrium condition and that Mr. B, who gives away a lower proportion of his property, has more money in the end. In fact, the amount of money in the equilibrium state is inversely proportional to the rate of giving away. Thus, since A's giving rate is 50 per cent and B's rate is 25 per cent, in the ratio 2:1, then A's money/B's in the equilibrium state is in the ratio 1:2, or A has one-third and B two-thirds. In still more general terms, let A's giving rate be μ and B's giving rate be ν. Suppose that A has a fraction p of the total money and B has $1 - p = q$ in the equilibrium state. The amount that A gives to B must be $p\mu$, and the amount that B gives to A must be $q\nu$; and these two amounts must balance each other in order to maintain the equilibrium. Solving the equation $p\mu = q\nu$, we obtain the general answer:

$$\frac{p}{q} = \frac{\nu}{\mu} \quad \text{or} \quad p:q = \nu:\mu$$

or
$$p = \frac{\nu}{\mu + \nu} \quad \text{and} \quad q = \frac{\mu}{\mu + \nu}$$

Stability and Speed

Let us point out another important property of the equilibrium. Table 7-1, Case II, shows that A has $110 and B has $190 after the second exchange. Now suppose that one interferes with the game and takes $100 from B by force and gives it to A, so that A will have $210 and B only $90. This is a setback for B, but he may accept this as a new initial condition. After one leaves the scene and they resume the game according to their original rule again, they will soon reach the same equilibrium condition (A, $100; B, $200) as if there had never been interference. The effect of interference imposed from outside is only temporary and does not affect the final equilibrium value. This kind of equilibrium is said to be *stable*. Whether A has less or more than $100 at any given time, he will always end up with $100 if the game continues long enough under the same rule.

Now consider a set of new rules. Mr. A gives 10 per cent of his money to Mr. B; in return, B gives 5 per cent of his money to A. From the general argument and solution given above, we conclude that the final equilibrium condition will be the same as before because the ratio of these two rates remain the same. The reader may use the initial condition of Case I to start the exchange process and satisfy himself that this is actually the case. When he does this, he will notice that with lower rates of exchange it takes much longer to reach the equilibrium condition. If A's giving rate is 2 per cent and B's giving rate is 1 per cent, it will take a large number of exchanges to reach the equilibrium state. The final result is, however, still the same, viz., A has $100 and B has $200. The only way to change the equilibrium value is to change the ratio of the two giving rates. For example, if the two giving rates, instead of being 2:1, are of the same magnitude, or 1:1 (e.g., both giving 25 per cent), then in the equilibrium state A and B will each have $150, or half the total, whatever it is.

THE GLOVE CLUB

Gloves and Type of Membership

There are 100 members in a Glove Club, but their gloves are quite assorted. Of the 100 left-hand gloves manufactured by Aaron Company, 70 are black and 30 white. Of the 100 right-hand gloves manufactured by Bebee Company, 40 are black and 60 white. No matter how these gloves are distributed among the members, if we look at their left hands alone, we will find 70 wearing black gloves and 30 white. Similarly, if we look at their right hands alone, we will find 40 wearing black gloves and 60 white. Since the number of the various kinds of gloves is fixed, the number of hands with black and white gloves is fixed accordingly, whatever the rule of distributing the gloves may be. However, if we look at the individuals, the rule of distributing the gloves would make a lot of difference. There are four types of individuals. Those wearing black gloves on both hands will be referred to as X type for short; those wearing black on the left hand and white on the right are referred to as Y type; and so on. These four types of membership are shown in Fig. 7-1.

Let us first consider a simple rule for distributing the gloves: the 100 lefts are distributed to the members at random and then the 100 rights are distributed, again at random. In the ideal case with which we are dealing, there will be 28 X-type individuals, 42 Y individuals, 12 Zs, and 18 Ws, as indicated at the bottom of Fig. 7-1. Note that among the 100 left hands there are $28 + 42 = 70$

wearing blacks and $12 + 18 = 30$ whites. Similarly, among the 100 right hands, there are $28 + 12 = 40$ with black gloves and $42 + 18 = 60$ with whites. To repeat, the rule of distributing the gloves determines the number of individuals (28, 42, 12, 18) in each of the four categories of membership, not the number of hands with black and white gloves. The latter are fixed by the asset of the club.

Having made the point on the constancy of black and white gloves, we shall henceforth suppose that the club membership is very large and talk about percentages or proportions instead of

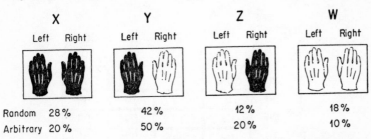

	X	Y	Z	W
	Left Right	Left Right	Left Right	Left Right
Random	28%	42%	12%	18%
Arbitrary	20%	50%	20%	10%

FIG. 7-1. Random and arbitrary distribution of left-hand gloves (70 per cent black and 30 per cent white) and right-hand gloves (40 per cent black and 60 per cent white) among the members of the Glove Club.

the absolute numbers. Thus, the ideal situation described above consists of $.28X, .42Y, .12Z, .18W$. We shall pair the members shortly.

Annual Dinner and Glove Trading

Suppose that for some reason or other the club did not at first distribute the gloves at random but somewhat arbitrarily, so there are 20 per cent X, 50 per cent Y, 20 per cent Z, 10 per cent W. Again, note that the proportion of hands with black and white gloves remains the same as before. If no member is allowed to trade gloves with other members, the proportions of the four types of individuals will remain .20, .50, .20, .10 year after year. However, the Glove Club, like all other organizations, holds an annual convention and dinner, and the members are allowed to trade gloves during the convention according to certain rules. At the convention the members are paired at random into dinner partners, each pair sitting at a separate table. Only the two members at the same table are permitted to trade one of their gloves; they are not obligated to do so, but they may if they want to. Let us assume that only 25 per cent of the dinner partners actually change one of their gloves and that the remaining 75 per cent prefer to keep what they have.

The initial club membership consists of .20 X, .50 Y, .20 Z, .10 W. Our first problem is to find out the proportion of each of the four types of individuals after the restricted exchange of gloves at the convention. The relative frequency of the various combinations of dinner partners or types of dining tables is shown below:

		X .20	Y .50	Z .20	W .10
X	.20	.04	.10	.04	.02
Y	.50	.10	.25	.10	.05
Z	.20	.04	.10	.04	.02
W	.10	.02	.05	.02	.01

Consider the table where an X member meets a Y. Mutual exchange of the left-hand black gloves results in no change. If X trades his right black for Y's right white, then the original X individual becomes a Y and the original Y becomes an X. The result is still one X and one Y and does not change the total proportion of the four types of membership in the club. Generally speaking, as long as the two dinner partners have one hand alike, either both black or both white, the trading of gloves between them causes no change in the proportion of membership type. Only when the two dinner partners differ with respect to both hands will an exchange of gloves have any effect. Such dining tables are where X meets W and Y meets Z (Fig. 7-2). There are 4 per cent of the former type and 20 per cent of the latter type among all the dining tables. The remaining 76 per cent of the tables do not contribute to the change of membership type.

The trading of either glove from X to W (Fig. 7-2) will change them into a Y and a Z. Conversely, at the other table, the exchange of either glove between Y and Z will change them into an X and a W. This is where and how the membership type changes.

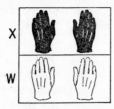

Frequency: .04   Frequency: .20

FIG. 7-2. The two types of dining tables where the trading of a glove between the partners changes the membership type. There are 4 per cent $X \cdot W$ tables and 20 per cent $Y \cdot Z$ tables at the first convention of the club.

Remembering the rule that only 25 per cent of the dinner partners actually do this sort of trading and 75 per cent of them keep what they have, we can calculate the total change in membership type as shown in Table 7-2.

TABLE 7-2. CHANGE OF MEMBERSHIP TYPE AFTER TRADING GLOVES AT THE DINNER TABLE

Type and frequency of dining table	With 25% trading				If there were no trading			
	X	Y	Z	W	X	Y	Z	W
$\frac{X}{W}$ or ●● / ○○ · · · · · .040	.015	.005	.005	.015	.020	0	0	.020
$\frac{Y}{Z}$ or ●○ / ○● · · · · · .200	.025	.075	.075	.025	0	.100	.100	0
Total........... .240	.04	.08	.08	.04	.02	.10	.10	.02

	X	Y	Z	W
Change due to trading..................	.02	− .02	− .02	.02
Original frequency......................	.20	.50	.20	.10
New value (original plus change).........	.22	.48	.18	.12
If entirely at random....................	.28	.42	.12	.18

The calculations in Table 7-2 are all in percentages. If there were no trading of gloves, the 4 per cent $X \cdot W$ table will, after the dinner, contribute 2 per cent X individuals and 2 per cent W individuals as before the dinner. Since one-quarter of them changed their membership type to Y and Z as a consequence of glove trading, these persons will consist of 1.5 per cent X type, .5 per cent Y type, etc. Note that the change (.02, $-.02$, $-.02$, .02) in the proportions of membership types, shown in Table 7-2, are the only changes during the annual dinner, because there have been no changes in the other tables. Adding these changes to the original frequency, we obtain the new proportions for the membership types after the annual convention. It is important to observe that these new values are somewhere in between the original and the ideal case of complete random distribution.

The Equilibrium State

Having learned how to calculate the new proportions of the membership types after one convention, we may continue the process and calculate the proportions after the second convention. If the reader does that, he should find that they are $.235X$, $.465Y$, $.165Z$, $.135W$. Note that these proportions are closer to those obtained through random distribution. What would be the final values if the Glove Club holds a convention year after year under the same rule? Let us look once more at the two critical types of tables (Fig. 7-2), which cause the change. A fraction of the persons at the $X \cdot W$ tables will become Y and Z after the dinner, and at the same time an equal fraction of the persons at the $Y \cdot Z$ tables will become X and W. This situation is very much like the one in the game of give and take between Mr. A and Mr. B described earlier in this chapter. Since the fraction of shifting between the two critical types of tables is the same, it follows that there will be no change in the proportion of membership types when the $X \cdot W$ and $Y \cdot Z$ tables are equally numerous. To express this condition in quantitative terms, let the lower-case x denote the proportion of the membership that is of the X type, etc. Then the frequency of $X \cdot W$ tables at the annual dinner, partners being paired at random, will be $2xw$ and that of $Y \cdot Z$ tables will be $2yz$. If there is to be no change in the proportions of membership type, the following condition must be satisfied:

$$xw = yz \quad (X \cdot W \text{ and } Y \cdot Z \text{ tables equal in frequency})$$

where $x + y = .70$ (70% of left-hand gloves are black)
$\quad\quad\quad x + z = .40$ (40% of right-hand gloves are black)

and $\quad x + y + z + w = 1$ (total of four membership types)

Substituting $w = 1 - x - y - z$ in the first equation, we have:

$$x(1 - x - y - z) = x - x^2 - xy - xz = yz$$
$$\therefore \quad x = x^2 + xy + xz + yz = (x + y)(x + z) = (.70)(.40) = .28$$

Then $y = .70 - x = .42$, $z = .40 - x = .12$, and the remainder $w = .18$. We see that:

$$xw = (.28)(.18) = .0504$$
and $\quad\quad\quad yz = (.42)(.12) = .0504$

also. These proportions are identical with those that would be achieved if the gloves were distributed to the members entirely at random. We may summarize the situation thus: *the annual limited trading of gloves between the random partners at certain dining tables will gradually lead to random distribution of the gloves.* When this state is reached, there will be no further change at later conventions.

This equilibrium is also stable. By that we mean, if you force certain members to trade their gloves and change the proportion of membership types arbitrarily, the disturbance is only temporary. When the members are allowed to hold their conventions under their old rules, they would gradually achieve the same random distribution again. The speed with which the equilibrium state is approached depends upon the fraction of dinner partners who trade gloves. In the example above, 25 per cent of the partners actually do the trading. If only 10 per cent trade, the approach to equilibrium would be slower. If 50 per cent of them do, the approach would be faster. All these properties are very similar to those of the simple game of give and take.

MULLER'S TRUCKING COMPANY

Rule of Buying and Junking

The model of equilibrium to be described in this section is borrowed from Prof. H. J. Muller (1950). Although it is directly applicable to simple genetic situations only, it does bring out some very fundamental features of equilibrium and the author knows of no better analogies. Suppose that a certain trucking company buys two new trucks every year and that these trucks can be used for only three years. At the end of the third year of service they will wear out sufficiently to cause them to be junked. How many trucks will the company have at hand in operating condition after a few years?

The buying and junking of the trucks is illustrated in Fig. 7-3. In the first year of operation (1951, say) the company has two new trucks of the '51 model, which are to last for three years. In the second year (1952) the company buys two new '52 model trucks and at the same time still has the two '51 trucks. In the third year the company will have six trucks, but in the fourth year the two '51 trucks are junked and two new '54 model trucks are bought, so the company still has six trucks on hand. It is seen that from now on the company will have six trucks every year, and this is the equilibrium condition. Every year the number of new trucks bought and the number of old trucks discarded exactly balance each other, so the number of trucks in the company remains the same year after year.

The equilibrium number of trucks, six in this example, may be viewed in two different ways. The direct way is to look at a particular column (year) of Fig. 7-3. For example, in 1955, the six trucks in service are of different ages: two are new models, two are 1 year old, and the remaining two are 2 years old. Alternatively, we may look at Fig. 7-3 horizontally, that is, following the two trucks of a given model for 3 years. Of these six trucks, two are new models, two are 1 year old, and the remaining two are 2 years old. The two different views are mathematically equivalent. In general, the equilibrium number is equal to the number of new trucks bought per year multiplied by the length of service life in years. Thus, in our example, $2 \times 3 = 6$.

Now suppose that one truck is stolen, so the company operates with five trucks instead of the usual six. If the stolen truck is a 2-year-old one, the company will have six trucks again the next year. If a new truck is stolen, the company will have to operate with five trucks for 3 years, but after that period the company will have six again. On the other hand, if a certain Rockfall

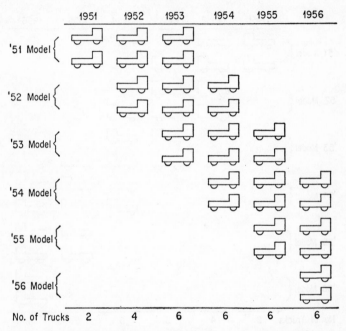

FIG. 7-3. Equilibrium number of trucks. The rules of operation are as follows: (1) two new trucks are bought each year, and (2) each truck has a service life of 3 years.

Foundation donates four new trucks and the company suddenly finds itself in possession of ten trucks instead of the usual six, the happy situation will last only for 3 years, and after that period the company will have the usual six again. In other words, this equilibrium is stable; disturbances from outside, either to increase or decrease the number of trucks, have only temporary effects. *The equilibrium number is determined solely by the rule of buying and length of service life.*

Varying Service Life

As before, let us suppose that the trucking company buys two new trucks every year, but now assume that one truck will last for 2 years and the other for 3 years. The situation has been illustrated in Fig. 7-4, which shows that the company has five trucks in the equilibrium condition. Consider the operations of the com-

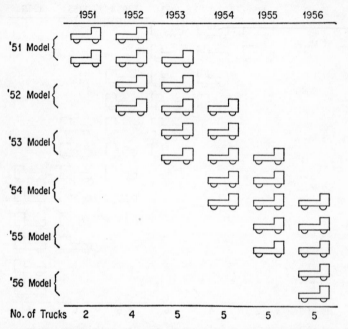

FIG. 7-4. Equilibrium number of trucks. The rules of operation are as follows: (1) two new trucks are bought each year, and (2) one truck lasts for 2 years and one truck lasts for 3 years, so the average service life is $2\frac{1}{2}$ years.

pany in 1954. Two new '54 model trucks are bought. Of the two discarded trucks, one is a '51 model that has completed 3 years of service and the other is a '52 model that has served for 2 years. Of the five trucks operating in 1954, two are new, two are 1 year old, and the remaining one is 2 years old, in its third year of service. With varying service life, the proportion of old trucks in operation is smaller than when all trucks last for 3 years. In the preceding example, the proportion of old trucks is $\frac{2}{6}$ and in the present case it is $\frac{1}{5}$.

As in the preceding example, the five trucks in the equilibrium condition (Fig. 7-4) may also be viewed in two ways: either vertically (trucks in a given year) or horizontally (trucks of a given model). Since a truck may last for 2 or 3 years, the average length of service life is $2\frac{1}{2}$ years. Applying the general method of finding the equilibrium number, we have $2 \times 2\frac{1}{2} = 5$.

It should be emphasized that in both examples the number of new trucks to be bought each year and the length of service life of the trucks are two independent rules and have no necessary relationship with each other. Each rule determines a separate feature of the equilibrium condition. Once we decide to buy two new trucks each year, it implies that in the equilibrium state two trucks must be eliminated each year, whatever the length of service life may be. In other words, the rule of buying directly determines the *number* of trucks to be eliminated each year in the equilibrium state. On the other hand, the length of service life tells us the *age* at which a truck is to be junked, or the length of time it serves the company. The longer the service life, the more trucks will be accumulated in the company. Since the buying rule of the two trucking companies above is the same, the number of trucks discarded by them each year is also the same. The difference in equilibrium condition between the two companies lies solely in the difference between the service life of the trucks they buy. When we put the two features—buying and service life— together, we obtain the whole picture of the equilibrium state. We will know not only the equilibrium number of trucks but also the age or model of the trucks at hand in any given year.

UNSTABLE EQUILIBRIUM

Equal Contribution and Matching

All the models described so far have a stable equilibrium. In this and the next section we shall consider examples of an entirely different type of equilibrium. Suppose that Mr. A owns 40 per cent of the stock of a certain company and Mr. B owns 60 per cent. Now A decides to contribute half his wealth to a charitable organization, and B offers to match his contribution; that is, to donate an equal amount of money for charity. After the contribution, the ratio of A's wealth to B's becomes 2:4 instead of the original 4:6, as shown in Table 7-3. Assume that the company prospers and that the contribution does not affect the business or assets of the company. Changing the ratio after contribution into ordinary percentages, we see that A now owns 33.3 per cent of the company's stock. If the rule of contribution and matching continues year after year, Table 7-3 shows that the wealth of

TABLE 7-3. RESULTS OF EQUAL CONTRIBUTION*

Relative Wealth		Contribution from each	Ratio after Contribution	
Mr. A	Mr. B		A:B	Total
.400	.600	.200	.200: .400	.600
.333	.667	.166	.167: .501	.668
.250	.750	.125	.125: .625	.750
.167	.833	.083	.084: .750	.834
.100	.900	.050	.050: .850	.900
. . . .	. . . . .	. . . .	. . . . :	. . . . .
0	1.000	0	0 :1.000	1.000

* The rule is that Mr. A contributes half of what he has and Mr. B matches his contribution (puts up an equal amount).

Mr. A relative to Mr. B is steadily decreasing, approaching 0 as the limit. The reason is simple. The amount of contribution (or tax), being equal for both, always hurts the poorer fellow more than the wealthier one. The contribution takes more, proportionally, from A than from B. Hence, percentagewise, equal contribution will make the poorer one still poorer and the wealthier one still wealthier.

However, there is one situation in which equal contribution does not affect the relative wealth of A and B; that is when they are equally rich. It is easy to see (that is, it is easy to see in this case) that, if A and B each own 50 per cent of the stock, equal contributions of any amount, as long as they are equal, will not affect their relative wealth. Hence we say that 50:50 is an equilibrium condition under the rule of equal contribution.

This equilibrium state differs from all the preceding ones in one fundamental feature; viz., it is affected irrecoverably by disturbances. As long as A and B are exactly equal in wealth, equal contribution will keep them that way year after year. But a slight deviation from the ideal 50:50 situation will result in a greater deviation. The equilibrium cannot restore itself from disturbance. Even if the initial condition is that A has .498 and B has .502, equal contribution will gradually reduce A's percentage to zero. The equilibrium condition 50:50, though very close, can never be reached again. This type of equilibrium is known as *unstable*. By the very nature of unstableness,we do not expect to find that such equilibria exist for any length of time in the real world.

Double Matching

If equal contribution is unfair to the poorer fellow, how about double matching? Suppose that A contributes a certain amount by a certain rule and then B contributes twice that amount. Table 7-4 shows an example of this situation. The initial condition

TABLE 7-4. RESULTS OF DOUBLE MATCHING*

Relative Wealth		Contribution from		Ratio after Contribution	
Mr. A	Mr. B	Mr. A	Mr. B	A:B	Total
.300	.700	.150	.300	.150: .400	.550
.273	.727	.136	.273	.137: .454	.591
.232	.768	.116	.232	.116: .536	.652
.178	.822	.089	.178	.089: .644	.733
.121	.879	.060	.121	.061: .758	.819
....	.....	....	....	....:.....	.....
0	1.000	0	0	0:1.000	1.000

* The rule is that Mr. A contributes half of what he has and Mr. B double matches his contribution.

is that A has 30 per cent and B, 70 per cent. Calculation shows that A's wealth, percentagewise, still decreases year after year, approaching 0 as limit. The reason again is very simple. Mr. B has more than twice as much as Mr. A in the beginning; the contribution and double matching still takes, proportionally, more from A than from B. The system of double matching has, however, slowed down the rate at which A's relative wealth diminishes.

Again, there is a situation in which the rule of double matching leaves the relative wealth of A and B unchanged; that is when B has exactly twice as much as A has. When A has one-third and B two-thirds of the total, the double matching of contribution does not change the ratio of A's wealth to B's. Needless to say, this equilibrium is also unstable. The only difference between equal contribution and double matching is that in the former case the equilibrium state is $A:B = 1:1$, and in the latter case it is $A:B = 1:2$. As an exercise, the reader may show that if the initial condition is A, .40 and B, .60, the system of double matching by B will soon reduce B's asset to 0, because he does not have twice as much as A in the beginning. The purpose of this example is to show that an unstable equilibrium is not necessarily at the point ($\frac{1}{2}$, $\frac{1}{2}$) but could be of any value, depending on the rules of contribution.

It is clear from the above examples that for an unstable equilibrium the initial condition is very important. The initial financial status of A and B determines which one of them will eventually go broke under a certain rule of contribution.

Summary

In the first model the total amount of money between A and B is fixed. In the second model the number of the various kinds of gloves is fixed. In these two models the problem is entirely a matter of distribution according to certain rules. In the third model, that of the trucking company, there are new additions as well as eliminations. In all these three models, the equilibrium condition is stable; the initial condition of the game plays no part in determining the final result; disturbances have only temporary effects; the equilibrium condition is determined solely by the rules of operation. In the fourth model there is the elimination process without new additions, and the equilibrium is unstable. It tilts whenever there is a slight disturbance; the direction of the tilting depends on the initial condition or the direction of the disturbance imposed on the condition.

Should an addition process be introduced to the unstable equilibrium of the last model, the result may become stable or remain unstable, depending on the exact rule of giving new money to A and B. The stability of an equilibrium has to be studied individually for each set of rules.

There are many different situations that would lead to stable or unstable equilibrium, but these four examples must suffice. The main purpose of this chapter is to acquaint the beginner with some of the general features of equilibrium, so that when he encounters a more or less similar situation in genetics (analogies are never exact in details), he will be better equipped to comprehend it.

Chapter 8
Two Pairs of Loci and Linkage

Each chromosome has a great number of loci, and there are 23 pairs of chromosomes in man. For two loci chosen at random (A,a and B,b, say), the chances are that they are located on different pairs of chromosomes. If they are located on the same chromosome, they are said to be *linked*. The term *linkage* in genetics is a very technical one; it merely means that two loci are located on the same chromosome pair and nothing else. The physical fact that two loci are on the same chromosome causes positive or negative correlation between the two traits they control among the children of certain families. Hence the term linkage. A considerable portion of this chapter is devoted to showing that genetic linkage of two loci causes *no* correlation between the hereditary traits they control in the population as a whole. When this point is made very clear, we will briefly discuss a method of detecting linkage from sib-pair data.

Crossover and Linkage in Families

When genes A and B are on one chromosome and a and b on another, the genotype will be written as AB/ab. If the two genes on the same chromosome always stay together, the individual AB/ab will produce only two kinds of gametes: AB and ab. Breeding experiments and cytologic observations show that there is usually a certain amount of *crossover* (or crossing over) between the two chromosomes in the interval between the two loci, so Ab and aB gametes are also produced, only in a smaller proportion. The proportion of such gametes is called the percentage of *recombination* or simply *crossover value*. On the other hand, if the two loci are on two different pairs of chromosomes, the double-heterozygote individual will produce four types of gametes in equal proportions on account of independent assortment of chromosomes in meiosis. This is equivalent to having 50 per cent crossovers for linked genes. The situation may be summarized as follows, where c = percentage of recombination.

Genotype	Coupling: AB/ab				Repulsion: Ab/aB			
Gametes	AB	Ab	aB	ab	AB	Ab	aB	ab
$c = 0$	.50	0	0	.50	0	.50	.50	0
$c = 20\%$	.40	.10	.10	.40	.10	.40	.40	.10
$c = 50\%$	.25	.25	.25	.25	.25	.25	.25	.25

Note that genetic linkage does not mean that the certain two genes always stay together on the same chromosome. In one individual, A and B are linked, whereas in another, A and b are. Therefore, linkage applies to two loci rather than any two particular alleles.

There are nine genotypes with respect to two loci, each with two alleles, but as far as the production of gametes is concerned, we need only to consider the double-heterozygote individual because linkage makes no difference to the other eight genotypes. For instance, Ab/ab would produce 50 per cent Ab and 50 per cent ab gametes whether the loci are linked or independent. To study linkage, at least one of the parents must be double heterozygous.

It is easier to study linkage for genes without dominance (where the genotype is known) than for genes with dominance. In the latter case it is much easier to detect linkage for a rare dominant gene than for a recessive. Linkage in the coupling phase (AB/ab) is easier to detect than in the repulsion phase (Ab/aB). The detection of linkage largely depends on deviation of segregation ratio among children of certain types of families from that expected on the basis of independent assortment. Close linkage is therefore easier to detect than loose linkage. Large families are especially valuable for linkage studies. A family of 10 children is worth many times (for statistical purposes) a family of 3. It is

due to these and many other difficulties that linkage study in m
is a slow process.

In Fig. 8-1 are two simplified hypothetical families to sh◖
how linkage can be detected from family pedigrees. They conc◖
the linkage between the ABO locus and the locus for nail-pat◖
syndrome. (In the pedigree B ≡ I^B, the allele of the blood gr◖
locus, not to be confused with the second pair (B,b) of genes ◖
ferred to earlier.) The nail-patella syndrome and the ABO ▮
are closely linked. The syndrome is a rare dominant trait w◖

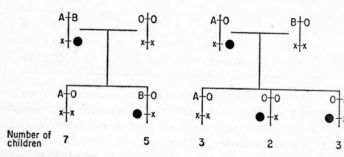

Number of children   7   5   3   2   3

FIG. 8-1. Two families showing linkage between the blood group ABO lo◖
and the nail-patella syndrome gene, denoted by the solid circle ●; its nor◖
(recessive) allele is denoted by a small cross ×. For details, see Renw◖
and Lawler (1955) and Jameson, Lawler, and Renwick (1956). In◖
first family all B children have the nail-patella syndrome and all A c◖
dren are normal. In the second family, the syndrome appears only◖
O and B children but not in A, showing that the syndrome gene is on◖
O-chromosome.

regular transmission, and its possessors are known to be hete◖
zygous. Genotype of an AB individual is known, and the ot◖
parent is a double recessive. Both families are large. Furthermo◖
in one family the syndrome gene is on the B-chromosome, and◖
the other it is on the O-chromosome. This is characteristic◖
genetic linkage in contradistinction to physiologic association,◖
pleiotropism. It is a combination of these fortunate circumstan◖
that these two pedigrees together constitute an irrevocable pr◖
of linkage of the two loci. For other examples of linkage ◖
reader may consult Roberts (1959, Chap. VIII) and Stern (19◖
Chaps. 14 and 15).

Gene Distribution in an Equilibrium Population

Before reading this section it is well for the reader to review the section on The Glove Club, Chap. 7, and get thoroughly familiar with the rules of the club and the consequences of an annual convention. Now, to understand the situation for two loci in a random-mating population, we need only to make the following translations. The first pair of alleles (A, a) is identified with left-hand gloves manufactured by Aaron Company and the second locus (B, b) with right-hand gloves manufactured by Bebee Company. Let A and B alleles stand for black gloves and a and b for white ones. Then the four types of membership are the four types of chromosomes (or gametes):

$$\underset{X}{\overset{\displaystyle A \quad\quad B}{\vdash\!\!\!\!\!-\!\!\!\!\!\dashv}} \quad \underset{Y}{\overset{\displaystyle A \quad\quad b}{\vdash\!\!\!\!\!-\!\!\!\!\!\dashv}} \quad \underset{Z}{\overset{\displaystyle a \quad\quad B}{\vdash\!\!\!\!\!-\!\!\!\!\!\dashv}} \quad \underset{W}{\overset{\displaystyle a \quad\quad b}{\vdash\!\!\!\!\!-\!\!\!\!\!\dashv}}$$

The random pair of dinner partners at an annual convention is a genotype (in a random-mating population). For instance, the dinner table X/W is the genotype AB/ab and Y/Z is Ab/aB. Exchange of gloves at the dinner table is crossover. Each annual convention is equivalent to one generation of random mating. If the reader makes these translations and rereads about the Glove Club, he cannot fail to understand why two linked genes are distributed at random as if they were independent in a random-mating population. For the sake of clarity, however, a brief paraphrase of the process of approaching equilibrium is given here in genetic language.

Let x be the frequency of AB chromosomes, etc., and $x + y + z + w = 1$. Consider any arbitrary initial population in which the initial chromosome frequencies are x_0, y_0, z_0, w_0; for instance,

$$x_0 = .20 \qquad y_0 = .50 \qquad z_0 = .20 \qquad w_0 = .10$$

If we consider the (A, a) locus alone, the gene frequencies are:

$$p = x_0 + y_0 = .70 \qquad q = z_0 + w_0 = .30$$

Similarly, if the (B, b) locus is considered alone, the gene frequencies are:

$$u = x_0 + z_0 = .40 \qquad v = y_0 + w_0 = .60$$

These gene frequencies are fixed, and they do not change fro generation to generation (the number of black and white glov are fixed), although the chromosome frequencies do change account of crossovers.

Random mating of individuals is equivalent to random uni of gametes (Chap. 2). Hence, proportions of various genotypes the next generation are given by the terms of:

$$(x_0 + y_0 + z_0 + w_0)^2$$

This is equivalent to the frequency of types of dining tables giv on p. 108. From these genotypic proportions and allowing f crossovers in double-heterozygote individuals, the chromoson frequencies (x_1, y_1, z_1, w_1) after the first generation of random ma ing may be calculated. The step-by-step arithmetic has be given in Table 7-2, in which the crossover value is taken to $c = .25$. If the reader cares to rewrite the arithmetic in terms symbols, he will find that the new frequency of AB chromosome i

$$\begin{aligned} x_1 &= x_0 + (1 - c)x_0w_0 + cy_0z_0 - x_0w_0 \\ &= x_0 - c(x_0w_0 - y_0z_0) \end{aligned}$$

Example: $x_1 = .20 - .25(.02 - .10) = .22$

as obtained previously. In fact, we need only calculate this o frequency, as $x_1 + y_1 = p$ and $x_1 + z_1 = u$, etc., are fixed value From the numerical example on the exchange of gloves we s that, after each generation of random mating, the chromoson frequencies come closer to those expected on the basis of rando distribution. They will remain unchanged only if AB/ab al Ab/aB are equally frequent in the population, because they a the only ones that make the chromosome frequencies chang Hence the equilibrium condition is:

$$\begin{aligned} \text{freq(AB/ab)} &= \text{freq(Ab/aB)} \quad \text{or} \quad xw = yz \\ x(1 - x - y - z) &= x - x^2 - xy - xz \quad = yz \\ \therefore x = x^2 + xy + xz + yz &= (x + y)(x + z) \quad = pu \end{aligned}$$

that is,   freq(AB chromosome) = freq(A gene) × freq(B gene)

Similarly, $y = pv$, $z = qu$, and $w = qv$ at equilibrium.

If the two loci are on two different pairs of chromosomes, the equilibrium condition is the same, which may thus be summarized as:

$$(p \, A + q \, a)(u \, B + v \, b) = pu \, AB + pv \, Ab + qu \, aB + qv \, ab$$

Example:

$$(.7 \, A + .3 \, a)(.4 \, B + .6 \, b) = .28 \, AB + .42 \, Ab + .12 \, aB + .18 \, ab$$

The only difference between two linked and two independent genes is in the rate of approaching equilibrium and not in the final condition. This is illustrated in Table 8-1.

TABLE 8-1. THE APPROACH TO EQUILIBRIUM FOR TWO LOCI IN
A RANDOM-MATING POPULATION

Generation	Linkage of Two Loci with 25% Crossover					Two Independent Loci (50% Crossover)				
	AB x	Ab y	aB z	ab w	|dev|	AB x	Ab y	aB z	ab w	|dev|
0	.20	.50	.20	.10	.08	.20	.50	.20	.10	.08
1	.22	.48	.18	.12	.06	.24	.46	.16	.14	.04
2	.235	.465	.165	.135	.045	.26	.44	.14	.16	.02
3	.246	.454	.154	.146	.034	.27	.43	.13	.17	.01
Limit	.28	.42	.12	.18	0	.28	.42	.12	.18	0

The chromosome frequencies listed in Table 8-1 may be calculated either after the manner shown in Table 7-2 or by using the formula for x_1 repeatedly. The |dev| in the table is $|xw - yz|$, and it is also the deviation of chromosome frequencies of any generation from those of the equilibrium state; e.g., for Ab chromosome, $.50 - .42 = .08$. We see that for two independent genes the deviation from equilibrium is halved in each generation; the approach to equilibrium is very rapid. For linked genes with c crossover, the deviation is reduced by c in each generation. Thus, when $c = .25$, the deviation of the next generation is 75 per cent of the previous one. The rate of approach to equilibrium depends upon the degree of linkage. In our example, the deviation from equilibrium after 15 generations will be $(.08)(.75)^{15} = .001$.

From a broader point of view, it is rather fortunate that genetic linkage of loci does *not* cause association of corresponding traits in a population; for if it did, the human traits could then be classified into 23 associated groups and would greatly impair the existing vast diversity of phenotypes. To facilitate the precise process of meiosis, the genes are organized into chromosomes, and yet they are distributed in the population as if they were independent. Such is the subtlety of Nature.

Genotype and Phenotype Proportions

Since the equilibrium frequencies of the four types of gametes are known, the nine genotypic proportions may be easily calculated by combining the gametes at random. The reader may first construct a 4×4 checkerboard with $pu(AB)$, $pv(Ab)$, $qu(aB)$, $qv(ab)$ as the four row and four column totals and then collect the 16 combinations into nine genotypes. On account of the relation:

$$AB \quad Ab \quad aB \quad ab \qquad A \quad a \quad B \quad b$$
$$(pu + pv + qu + qv)^2 = (p + q)^2(u + v)^2$$

the proportions may also be obtained by merely constructing a 3×3 checkerboard, as shown in Table 8-2A. The number of

TABLE 8-2. PROPORTIONS OF GENOTYPES AND PHENOTYPES IN AN EQUILIBRIUM POPULATION WITH RESPECT TO TWO PAIRS OF GENES

	A. Nine genotypes					*B. Four phenotypes*		
	BB	Bb	bb			B-	bb	
AA	p^2u^2	$2p^2uv$	p^2v^2	p^2	A-	$(1-q^2)(1-v^2)$	$(1-q^2)v^2$	$1-q^2$
Aa	$2pqu^2$	$4pquv$	$2pqv^2$	$2pq$				
aa	q^2u^2	$2q^2uv$	q^2v^2	q^2	aa	$q^2(1-v^2)$	q^2v^2	q^2
	u^2	$2uv$	v^2	1.00		$1-v^2$	v^2	1.00

phenotypes depends upon dominance and interaction of the two pairs of alleles. If A is dominant to a, and B dominant to b, and there is no interaction, there will be four phenotypes (A-B-,

A-bb, aaB-, aabb), as shown in Table 8-2B. The marginal totals are the proportions for a single locus. Let the symbol (A-B-) denote the proportion of the double dominant phenotype, etc. From the four phenotypes the gene frequency of each locus may be estimated. Thus,

$$q = \sqrt{(aaB-) + (aabb)} = \sqrt{(aa)}$$
$$v = \sqrt{(A - bb) + (aabb)} = \sqrt{(bb)}$$

The four phenotype proportions also have the following relation:

$$(A\text{-}B\text{-})(aabb) = (A\text{-}bb)(aaB\text{-})$$

showing once more that there is no association between the two traits even if the two loci were linked.

Epistasis

The interaction between loci is called *epistasis*, which may take a great variety of patterns, especially when both loci affect the same trait (e.g., skin pigmentation). The genetic study of man is still mostly on a monofactorial level, and epistasis is not too well known. In Table 8-3 are listed some common types of interaction to show why it is difficult to demonstrate in man. The algebraic expressions for phenotype proportions are omitted in Table 8-3 because it is quite obvious what they should be by inspecting Table 8-2. Some of the terms or names for each type of epistasis, such as *recessive epistasis*, are tentative and hardly standardized, whereas others, such as *complementary* and *duplicate* are in common use. The term *inhibitor*, a gene that prevents expression of the effect of another locus, is also frequently used in genetic literature. In order to identify the epistasis pattern shown in Table 8-3 with the classic Mendelian ratios in F_2 generation (offspring of AaBb $\times$ AaBb), the ratios are given in parentheses under each pattern. These ratios may be used as codes or names to denote the various types of epistasis. In fact, if gene frequencies $p = q = u = v = \frac{1}{2}$, the phenotypes will be in the ratios indicated in parentheses. The F_2 ratios may thus be regarded as a special case of the phenotype ratios in a random-mating population.

The three epistasis patterns in the first row of Table 8-3 yield three phenotypes each, and the patterns in the second row have only two phenotypes each. Let us examine some of them more closely. When bb suppresses the action of A, so all genotypes

TABLE 8-3. PHENOTYPES WHEN THERE IS
EPISTASIS (INTERACTION BETWEEN LOCI)

Recessive epistasis	Incomplete duplicate	Dominant epistasis
(9:3:4)	(9:6:1)	(12:3:1)
Complementary	Mutual epistasis	Duplicate
(9:7)	(13:3)	(15:1)

containing bb are of one phenotype, we have the (9:3:4) type of epistasis. The three phenotypes (A-B-, aaB-, bb) are in general of the proportions:

$$(1 - q^2)(1 - v^2) \qquad q^2(1 - v^2) \qquad v^2$$

However, if the two gene frequencies are such that $q^2 = 2v/(1 + v)$, the phenotype proportions become:

$$(1 - v)^2 \qquad 2v(1 - v) \qquad v^2$$

which are indistinguishable from Hardy-Weinberg proportions for one pair of genes without dominance. It follows that, when three phenotypes are of binomial proportions, it does not always imply that it is monofactorial inheritance. In genetic studies of animals and plants, test breeding is necessary. Analogously, in genetic studies of man, collection of pedigrees is necessary. In this particular example, if it is monofactorial, both A-B- and bb phenotypes should breed true; if it is recessive epistasis between two loci, none of them would. These two cases differ in breeding behavior but not necessarily in phenotype proportions in the population.

What has been said about the (9:3:4) type of epistasis is even more true for the (9:6:1) type under the name *incomplete duplicate* in Table 8-3. Perhaps *dominance additive* will also do. Here, the three phenotypes could very well be three grades of a qualitative trait (e.g., color) or of a quantitative trait (e.g., amount of some chemical substance in man). Genotypes with both dominant genes (A-B-) form the category of the highest grade; genotypes with one dominant gene (A-bb or aaB-) form the next category; and genotypes without any dominant gene constitute the third. The phenotype proportions are, respectively,

$$(1 - q^2)(1 - v^2) \qquad q^2(1 - v^2) + (1 - q^2)v^2 \qquad q^2v^2$$

If $q = v$, these three proportions are again indistinguishable from Hardy-Weinberg proportions. In other words, if the dominant genes of two loci have the same effect, i.e., additive, and have approximately the same frequency in the population, the three phenotypes will have the ordinary binomial proportions. Furthermore, their breeding behavior is also very similar to the monofactorial case, except that the phenotype with two dominant genes does not breed true. However, when frequencies of the dominant genes are low, the great majority of families in the population will behave in a way that is consistent with monofactorial inheritance.

By *dominant epistasis* is meant that the presence of B gene inhibits all effects of the A, a locus; this is the (12:3:1) type of epistasis shown in the table. Without going into details, it suffices

to point out that in this case it is also possible for the three phenotypes to be in binomial proportions $[v = 2q/(1 + q^2)]$.

If it is difficult, without the benefit of controlled mating, to
demonstrate epistasis with three phenotypes, it would be even
more difficult to do so with only two phenotypes (second row of
Table 8-3). In the latter case, even the estimation of the two gene
frequencies is impossible, and probably the most fruitful approach
is to examine large pedigrees. Let us call the phenotype A-B-
dominant and the other phenotype recessive for the (9:7) type of
complementary factors. The evidence for complementary factors
is that all three types of mating are capable of producing both
dominant and recessive offspring. This is not the case for monofactorial inheritance.

Finally, for duplicate factors, only the double recessive is different from the others, because one dominant gene (A or B) is as
good as two, three, or four. The two phenotype proportions are
$1 - q^2v^2$ and q^2v^2. This is the case briefly referred to in Chap. 3,
under Multiple Recessiveness. Writing Q for qv, we see that this
case is identical with monofactorial inheritance for all three types
of mating.

Epistasis has been discussed in some detail for several reasons.
One is to show the difficulty of studying it without controlled
breeding. Another is to point out the many possibilities of interaction between loci so human geneticists will not always confine
themselves to one locus. Real advances can be made in this direction if they do not always try to say "this gene is dominant" or
"that is recessive." All the types of epistasis shown in Table 8-3
are well known and quite common in mammals, poultry, other
animals, and plants, and there is no reason why they are not so in
man. The only well-known case of epistasis in man is the interaction between "secretor," ABO, and Lewis loci. Indeed, there is
much fragmentary evidence in human genetics *for* epistasis and
against the monofactorial hypothesis. For instance, albinism in
man is usually accepted as a simple recessive trait. But it is also
known that not all albinism is inherited in the same way. Some
albinism is apparently due to a dominant inhibitor rather than a
recessive homozygote. Diabetes mellitus is also regarded as a simple recessive trait by some investigators, but the fact that

diabetes $\times$ diabetes parents can produce nondiabetic offspring (beyond the usual age of onset) suggests that it might be due to the absence of one of the complementary factors or to some other similar mechanism. Right- or left-handedness is apparently not a monofactorial trait, because, although two right-handed parents can produce left-handed children, two left-handed parents can also produce right-handed children. This, again, suggests complementary factors. There is some evidence that the sickle hemoglobin genes (SS) inhibit the production of haptoglobins. Biochemical genetics of "errors" in metabolism (Hsia, 1959) should be a rich field in which interaction between loci can be discovered and studied. Advances in this direction will greatly enrich our understanding, not only of the mode of inheritance of a hereditary trait, but also the mode of action of the gene.

Sib-pair Method of Detecting Linkage

Estimating the proportion of recessive offspring from dominant parents (Chap. 5) is not as simple as it first sounds. Linkage study is based not only on the segregation ratio of one pair of alleles but on the deviation from the expected ratios of two pairs of alleles. The reader may understand why the methods of estimating linkage are so complicated. It is no coincidence that the workers who developed the methods of estimating linkage are the same group of biometricians mentioned at the end of Chap. 5, namely, Bernstein, Hogben, Fisher, Finney, Haldane, Bailey, Smith, Morton, etc. There is a certain amount of analogy between linkage methods and methods of determining recessive ratio. To explain these methods systematically is no minor task, and to use them requires a number of tables (analogous to our requirement of Table 5-2). Furthermore, the method varies from case to case, depending on the amount of information available about parents and grandparents, type of mating, dominance, and gene frequency. Under these circumstances the author chooses to expose but one comparatively simple method of detecting linkage, viz., the method of sib pairs developed by Penrose (1935, 1946). For an example of Fisher's method, the reader may consult Mather (1951, chap. X).

Since there are 23 pairs of chromosomes in man and far more than 23 loci are known in human genetics, some of them are necessarily linked, i.e., located on the same pair of chromosomes. Yet there is only a paucity of established cases of linkage reported up to date. This is no doubt largely due to the many usual difficulties in human genetics, but it is also due to the fact that loosely linked genes are hardly detectable. In experimental genetics, it was the closely linked genes that were first discovered and studied; the linkage group increased as newly discovered linked genes were added. Consider the following chromosome diagram:

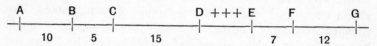

in which there is 10 per cent crossover between A and B loci, 5 per cent between B and C, and so on. If the loci A, B, C are studied, linkage may well be discovered. However, if A and F or G are studied directly, the result would be negative, showing no linkage even though they are on the same chromosome. It follows that the apparent independence between loci does not exclude the possibility that they still belong to the same *linkage group*. The linkage groups in animal and plant genetics are built up gradually by bridges of closely linked genes. At the present stage of our knowledge, the detection of linkage is probably a more immediate task than estimating the degree of linkage (except for sex-linked loci). The chances are that, whenever linkage is shown to exist, it is a strong one. Of course, there is no dividing line between close and loose linkage. The mid-point, 25 per cent crossover, may serve as a dividing line. In addition, the estimation of linkage is much more involved mathematically than the mere detection of it. In view of these facts, we shall confine ourselves to the detection rather than the estimation method. Also, there is a greater freedom in collecting data when the purpose is merely detection.

1. We shall consider the case of two loci with dominance but no interaction (Table 8-2B). There are four phenotypes in the population, viz.:

A-B-　　　　A-bb　　　　aaB-　　　　aabb

for example,

Tas, RH　　　　Tas, rh　　　　tas, RH　　　　tas, rh

where Tas = taster of PTC
    tas = nontaster
    RH = Rh positive
    rh = Rh negative

Each individual belongs to one of these four phenotypes. When a pair of siblings are considered, however, there are nine combinations. With respect to their ability to taste PTC (the first trait), the two siblings may be both tasters, one taster and one nontaster, or both nontasters. With respect to the Rh type (the second trait), they may be both positive, one positive and one negative, or both negative. Therefore, sib pairs can be classified into 3 × 3 combinations when two traits are considered simultaneously. This is done in Table 8-4 when a numerical example is considered.

2. There are 45 types of mating for nine genotypes. Of these, only 4 produce linkage effect in the distribution of sib pairs. These 4 types of discriminating families and their frequencies in population are:

$$\text{AaBb} \times \text{aabb: freq } f_1 = 2(4pquv)q^2v^2$$
$$\text{AaBb} \times \text{Aabb: freq } f_2 = 2(4pquv)2pqv^2$$
$$\text{AaBb} \times \text{aaBb: freq } f_3 = 2(4pquv)2q^2uv$$
$$\text{AaBb} \times \text{AaBb: freq } f_4 = (4pquv)^2$$

In each of these families, the distribution of sib pairs is determined by the crossover value and therefore is different from that for independent loci. The closer the linkage, the greater the difference. All other types of families produce the same distribution of sib pairs whether the loci are linked or not. Now the reader sees another reason why even the detection of linkage requires a large number of random sib pairs, because the linkage effect is largely masked by families without linkage effect. In experimental studies of linkage geneticists always use parents of genotypes shown above so that all their experimental families yield information on linkage. Human geneticists have to take all families, many of which are useless for linkage studies. AaBb × AaBb is indistinguishable phenotypically from AABB × AABB, etc., unless there is segregation for both traits. It is also clear from the mating frequencies f_1, f_2, etc., that it is easier to detect linkage when the dominant genes are rare, for then the four types of discriminating families will be proportionally more numerous in the population than otherwise. It is very difficult to demonstrate linkage for rare recessives.

3. Of the four discriminating types of families shown above, the most informative one (i.e., yielding the largest linkage effect) is AaBb × aabb. It is also the easiest to handle. We shall illus-

TABLE 8-4. TYPES OF SIB PAIRS PRODUCED BY AaBb × aabb PARENTS CROSSOVER VALUE $c = .20$

Parents		Coupling AB/ab × ab/ab				Repulsion Ab/aB × ab/ab			
Sib pairs		AB/ab .40	Ab/ab .10	aB/ab .10	ab/ab .40	AB/ab .10	Ab/ab .40	aB/ab .40	ab/ab .10
AB/ab	.40	.16	.04	.04	.16	.01	.04	.04	.01
Ab/ab	.10	.04	.01	.01	.04	.04	.16	.16	.04
aB/ab	.10	.04	.01	.01	.04	.04	.16	.16	.04
ab/ab	.40	.16	.04	.04	.16	.01	.04	.04	.01

Collecting these 16 combinations into 3 × 3 classes

First trait (A,a)	Second Trait (B, b)			Second Trait (B, b)			Total
	dom, dom (+,+)	dom, rec (+,−)	rec, rec (−,−)	dom, dom (+,+)	dom, rec (+,−)	rec, rec (−,−)	
dom, dom	.16	.08	.01	.01	.08	.16	.25
dom, rec	.08	.34	.08	.08	.34	.08	.50
rec, rec	.01	.08	.16	.16	.08	.01	.25
Total	.25	.50	.25	.25	.50	.25	1.00

	Average (coupling + repulsion)			If no linkage (c = .50)			
dom, dom	.0850	.0800	.0850	.0625	.1250	.0625	.25
dom, rec	.0800	.3400	.0800	.1250	.2500	.1250	.50
rec, rec	.0850	.0800	.0850	.0625	.1250	.0625	.25
Total	.25	.50	.25	.25	.50	.25	1.00

trate the principle of sib-pair method in detail for this type of family. There are two subtypes according to the phase of the double-heterozygote parent: coupling AB/ab and repulsion Ab/aB. In Table 8-4 are shown the steps of calculating the frequencies of various types of sib pairs from such families, taking crossover value to be $c = .20$.

The AB/ab parent produces four kinds of gametes (AB, Ab, aB, ab) in the proportions .40, .10, .10, .40. These are also the proportions for the four phenotypes of the children, because the other parent's gamete is always ab. The 4×4 checkerboard gives the frequencies of sib pairs. Some of them have the same phenotype combination. In collecting these 16 cells into a 3×3 table according to the two traits, a routine rule can be observed. The four cells in the upper left quadrant go to the first row, because these siblings are all dominant-dominant pairs with respect to the first trait (Tas, Tas). Similarly, the lower right quadrant becomes the third row. As to the second row, the dominant-recessive pair with respect to both traits is the sum of the four diagonal cells. The rest is obvious. The two 3×3 tables are constructed separately for the two subtypes of families. One is the mirror image of the other. Finally, these two tables are combined and averaged, yielding the total frequency of various types of sib pairs from AaBb $\times$ aabb family. The latter are to be compared with the corresponding frequencies of the same type of family without linkage.

4. If there is no linkage, the four types of gametes produced by the AaBb parent are equally numerous, each with frequency $\frac{1}{4}$. The distribution of sib pairs for this case is given in the lower right portion of Table 8-4. Comparing the average (coupling + repulsion) frequencies with those for independent loci, we obtain the following deviations:

From Table 8-4				*General notation*		
+.0225	−.0450	+.0225		$+L_1$	$-2L_1$	$+L_1$
−.0450	+.0900	−.0450		$-2L_1$	$+4L_1$	$-2L_1$
+.0225	−.0450	+.0225		$+L_1$	$-2L_1$	$+L_1$

The deviations are all multiples of one basic quantity $L_1 = .0225$, where the subscript 1 indicates the first type of discriminating family (AaBb × aabb). Note that the frequencies in the four corners and the center are larger, whereas those in the four side cells are smaller in the linkage case than in the independent case. This pattern of deviation is characteristic of genetic linkage and constitutes the basis for the detection method for sib-pair data.

5. The magnitude of L_1 depends on the crossover value. Replacing the gametic frequencies .40, .10, .10, .40 in our example by the general notation:

$$\tfrac{1}{2}(1 - c) \qquad \tfrac{1}{2}c \qquad \tfrac{1}{2}c \qquad \tfrac{1}{2}(1 - c)$$

and proceeding exactly the same way as outlined in Table 8-4, we obtain:

$$L_1 = \tfrac{1}{4}(\tfrac{1}{2} - c)^2$$

Putting $c = .20$, $L_1 = \tfrac{1}{4}(.50 - .20)^2 = .0225$, correctly. For the next two types of families (AaBb × Aabb and AaBb × aaBb), a similar procedure yields:

$$L_2 = L_3 = \tfrac{1}{16}(\tfrac{1}{2} - c)^2$$

showing that the linkage effect on sib pairs of these families is only $\tfrac{1}{4}$ of the first type. For the fourth type of family (AaBb × AaBb), there are three subtypes: $\tfrac{1}{4}$ (coupling × coupling), $\tfrac{1}{2}$ (coupling × repulsion), and $\tfrac{1}{4}$ (repulsion × repulsion), so three 3 × 3 tables for the sib pairs have to be constructed, pooled, and averaged. The result is:

$$L_4 = \tfrac{1}{16}(\tfrac{1}{2} - c)^2 [\tfrac{1}{2} + (\tfrac{1}{2} - c)^2]$$

The linkage effect of this type of family is even smaller. For $c = .20$, $L_4 = .0033$ approximately. For a random collection of sib pairs, the average value of these Ls is:

$$L = f_1 L_1 + f_2 L_2 + f_3 L_3 + f_4 L_4$$

which is a function of gene frequencies and crossover value. Since we do not attempt to estimate the degree of linkage, the explicit expression need not be given here. All the reader has to remember is that when there is no linkage, $L = 0$. Conversely, the closer the linkage, the greater the value of L.

6. We have also noticed, in the lower right portion of Table 8-4, that in the absence of linkage the frequencies of the various types of sib pairs are given by the corresponding product of marginal totals, the latter being the frequencies of sib pairs with respect to one trait separately. In the population as a whole, the distribution of sib pairs is the weighted average for all types of families, with or without linkage effect. The distribution is given in Table 8-5, in which, for the sake of simplicity, a, b, c are employed to denote the frequencies of the dominant-dominant, dominant-recessive, recessive-recessive sib pairs with respect to the first trait (tasting ability). These are the values given on p. 42, toward the end of Chap. 3. Thus, $a = S_{11}$, $b = S_{10}$, $c = S_{00}$. Similarly, x, y, z are the corresponding values for the second trait (Rh type). Linkage, of course, has no effect on the distribution of sib pairs with respect to any one trait separately.

With a given set of observed numbers (lower portion of Table 8-5), some estimate of L and its variance can be obtained, and

TABLE 8-5. FREQUENCY OF SIB PAIRS WITH RESPECT TO TWO TRAITS WITH DOMINANCE WHEN THERE IS LINKAGE

First trait (tasting ability)	Second trait (e.g., Rh type)			
	dom, dom	dom, rec	rec, rec	Total
dom, dom	$ax + L$	$ay - 2L$	$az + L$	a
dom, rec	$bx - 2L$	$by + 4L$	$bz - 2L$	b
rec, rec	$cx + L$	$cy - 2L$	$cz + L$	c
Total	x	y	z	1
	Corresponding observed numbers			
dom, dom	n_{11}	n_{12}	n_{13}	n_1
dom, rec	n_{21}	n_{22}	n_{23}	n_2
rec, rec	n_{31}	n_{32}	n_{33}	n_3
Total	n_1'	n_2'	n_3'	n

thus the hypothesis $L = 0$ can be tested. For numerical calculation it is convenient to work with nL rather than with the very small quantity L itself. Penrose's method follows.

7. First, a set of expected numbers E on the basis of no linkage is calculated. For instance, the expected number for the first cell is:

$$E_{11} = n(ax) = n\left(\frac{n_1}{n}\right)\left(\frac{n_1'}{n}\right) = \frac{n_1 \times n_1'}{n}$$

The expected numbers are based on the marginal totals alone and are the same numbers that would be calculated in an ordinary chi-square test. Second, calculate the ratios n_{11}/E_{11}, etc. If linkage exists, this ratio should be greater than unity for the four corner and the center cells but smaller than unity for the other four cells. The third step is to calculate the quantity:

$$W = \frac{n_{11}}{E_{11}} + \frac{n_{13}}{E_{13}} + \frac{n_{31}}{E_{31}} + \frac{n_{33}}{E_{33}} + \frac{4n_{22}}{E_{22}}$$
$$- 2\left(\frac{n_{12}}{E_{12}} + \frac{n_{21}}{E_{21}} + \frac{n_{23}}{E_{23}} + \frac{n_{32}}{E_{32}}\right)$$

In the ideal case, that is, if $n_{11} = n(ax + L)$, $E_{11} = n(ax)$, etc., the value of the expression above would be:

$$\overline{W} = 1 + \frac{L}{ax} - 2 + \frac{4L}{ay} + 1 + \frac{L}{az}$$
$$- 2 + \frac{4L}{bx} + 4 + \frac{16L}{by} - 2 + \frac{4L}{bz}$$
$$+ 1 + \frac{L}{cx} - 2 + \frac{4L}{cy} + 1 + \frac{L}{cz}$$
$$= L\left(\frac{1}{a} + \frac{4}{b} + \frac{1}{c}\right)\left(\frac{1}{x} + \frac{4}{y} + \frac{1}{z}\right)$$
$$= nL \cdot n\left(\frac{1}{n_1} + \frac{4}{n_2} + \frac{1}{n_3}\right)\left(\frac{1}{n_1'} + \frac{4}{n_2'} + \frac{1}{n_3'}\right)$$

Hence, W is an estimate of $\overline{W}$. If there is no linkage, W should fluctuate about zero. Finally, dividing W by the quantity:

$$I = n\left(\frac{1}{n_1} + \frac{4}{n_2} + \frac{1}{n_3}\right)\left(\frac{1}{n_1'} + \frac{4}{n_2'} + \frac{1}{n_3'}\right)$$

we obtain an estimate of nL. The variance of nL is simply $1/I$ and the standard error is $1/\sqrt{I}$. Hence, the hypothesis $nL = 0$ may be tested.

8. To illustrate the method, a numerical example of Penrose is reproduced in Table 8-6. The first trait is phenylketonuria, so

TABLE 8-6. OBSERVED AND EXPECTED NUMBERS OF SIB PAIRS
CLASSIFIED WITH RESPECT TO TWO TRAITS WITH
DOMINANCE (PENROSE, 1946)

First trait \\ Second trait	Observed numbers, n_{ij}			Total	1/total
	rec, rec	dom, rec	dom, dom		
rec, rec	37	7	1	45	.022,222
dom, rec	153	34	10	197	.020,305*
dom, dom	89	11	17	117	.008,547
Total	279	52	28	359	.051,074
1/total	.003,584	.076,923*	.035,714	.116,221	2.131 = I

Expected numbers, E_{ij}			Ratio n_{ij}/E_{ij}		
34.972	6.518	3.510	1.058	1.074	0.285
153.100	28.535	15.365	0.999	1.1915	0.651
90.928	16.947	9.125	0.979	0.649	1.863

* Four times the reciprocal.

that the recessive-recessive pairs are phenylketonuria-phenyl-ketonuria pairs. The second trait is ABO blood group. The presence of B antigen is regarded as the dominant trait (because it is comparatively rare), and the lack of it is considered recessive. Note that the order of dominant-dominant, dominant-recessive, and recessive-recessive is reversed, but this makes no difference on account of symmetry of the table. The arithmetic is set out systematically. From the sum of reciprocals of marginal totals (note $\frac{4}{197}$ and $\frac{4}{52}$) we find that:

$$I = 359(.051074)(.116221) = 2.131$$

and thus standard error of nL is $1/\sqrt{2.131} = 0.685$. The value of W is calculated from the table of ratios. Thus,

$$W = 1.058 + .285 + .979 + 1.863 + 4(1.1915)$$
$$- 2(1.974 + .999 + .651 + .649) = 2.205$$

Hence, the estimate of nL is:

$$nL = \frac{W}{I} = \frac{2.205}{2.131} = 1.035 \pm .685$$

The value of nL is only 1.51 times its standard error, and it is not significantly different from zero. The conclusion is that the linkage between phenylketonuria and ABO is not established, though the data are quite suggestive.

9. The linkage test outlined above is not merely a test for lack of independence between marginal distributions, as the chi-square test is. The W method of testing significance of nL is relevant to the specific pattern of deviations caused by linkage. The ordinary chi-square value for the data of Table 8-6 is $\chi^2 = 14.16$, with four degrees of freedom, and it is significant at the 1 per cent level. This merely indicates lack of independence, whatever direction the deviation may be. For a true linkage situation, however, the ratio n/E must be greater than unity for the four corner and the center cells. An examination of the ratios (lower part of Table 8-4) shows that two corner cells are inconsistent with linkage. The upper middle cell with ratio 1.074 is also inconsistent, as this ratio is expected to be smaller than unity. It is due to these inconsistencies that the linkage test yields an insignificant result. Of course, if linkage exists and all observed numbers are consistent, the chi-square test would also be valid, for, then, χ^2 is the same function of L^2 as W is of L. In general, however, the W method is preferred. This again stresses the difference between linkage and association.

10. The sib-pair method of detecting linkage is justified only when the information on a large number of sib pairs may be ob-

tained in a very convenient manner (as from school children) and when the phenotypes of the siblings' parents are unknown. In comparison with methods devised for data covering two generations or large pedigrees, the sib-pair method is less incisive. The literature on detection and estimation of linkage is voluminous. For a detailed account of the subject, showing the relations between the various methods, the reader may consult Smith (1953). Since then, a new scoring method for sequential tests has been developed by Morton (1955, 1957).

Chapter 9

Mutation and Selection

A systematic treatment of the vast field of mutation and selec-tion in natural populations would probably occupy a separate book of this size, because selection, like epistasis, operates in a great variety of ways, some simple and understandable and others that are subtle and still obscure to us. In this chapter no attempt is made to cover the subject in a comprehensive manner; rather, only a few fundamental principles are stressed; of these, the property of equilibrium is emphasized. Indeed, the subject of mutation and selection can hardly be discussed without an understanding of genetic equilibrium.

Balance between Mutations

Consider the alleles A_1 and A_2 of a certain locus. A mutation is a change of one allele to another (A_1 to A_2 or A_2 to A_1). The causes for mutation are largely unknown, and the direction of change is unpredictable. Nevertheless, mutation is a fact and has actually been observed and proved in many instances. Mutation arises in nature and must have a history as old as the gene. When an investigator reports a "new" mutation in man or any other organism, the student must not (although a layman often does) have the impression that something new has happened in the twentieth century. No, what the scientist means is that the mutation is new to him, in his material, and has not been previously reported by other investigators. Experimental study of mutation may be new, but mutation itself is not. Genes occasionally mutate whether they are studied or not. They are the ultimate source of hereditary diversity.

Furthermore, mutation is a rather regular phenomenon; the mutation rate in nature of any given allele is fairly constant. Some genes mutate more often than others, so each gene has its own characteristic mutation rate. The latter may be anywhere from 10^{-4} to 10^{-8} per generation. No accurate direct estimation of mutation rate for any human gene is possible, but estimates by indirect methods have been made. This will be discussed later in the chapter.

Suppose that $\mu = 6 \times 10^{-5}$ is the mutation rate of A_1 to A_2; that is, a proportion μ of the A_1 genes changes to A_2 every generation. If this is the only kind of mutation that occurs, then in due time all the genes in the population will be A_2; and when there is no A_1, there will be no more mutation either. This "one-way" (or unidirectional) change leads to a dead end. It is, however, more realistic to suppose that A_2 also mutates. Let the rate of mutation from A_2 to A_1 be $\nu = 3 \times 10^{-5}$. When both genes are capable of mutation at some fixed rates, what is the result in the population? The answer can be immediately given in the form of a simple mathematical formula, but what good does it do if the reader does not really see the mechanism at work?

To understand the effects of simultaneous mutations in opposite directions, the student may review the Game of Give and Take, in Chap. 7, identifying Mr. A with gene A_1, Mr. B with gene A_2, and the rules of exchange with the mutation rates. Everything that has been said about the give-and-take game applies to the situation of simultaneous mutations in opposite directions, so the student must reread that section, substituting genetic terms. The only difference between the two cases is in the magnitude of exchange (mutation) rate. A few highlights may be briefly reiterated here. Let p and q be the frequencies of A_1 and A_2 at any given generation. Then μp of the A_1 genes changes to A_2 and at the same time νq of the A_2 genes changes to A_1. The net change in p in one generation is $\mu p - \nu q$; and, at equilibrium, $\mu p = \nu q$. Hence, the final result is:

$$p = \frac{\nu}{\mu + \nu} \qquad q = \frac{\mu}{\mu + \nu}$$

In the present example, $p = 3/(6 + 3) = \frac{1}{3}$, and $q = \frac{2}{3}$ for the same reason stated in the give-and-take game. When this situation is reached, there will be no further change in gene frequency, although mutations in both directions continue to occur. The equilibrium value is determined by the mutation rates (rules of game) only and is independent of the initial conditions (see Case I and Case II of Table 7-1). This equilibrium is *stable*. If, for any reason at all, the frequency of A_1 is increased above the equilibrium value, the disturbance is only temporary and the frequency will eventually come down to the original equilibrium value, if the opposing mutation rates remain the same. These remarks are repeated here because they are the most important general properties of a genetic equilibrium.

Definition of Selection and Fitness

Millions, if not billions, of words have been written about natural selection, struggle for existence, survival of the fittest, adaptation, progress, etc., by a large number of writers. Some of them are attempting to reconstruct the history of man; some are trying to assure his future; but it seems that most of them have to some degree personal, arbitrary, subjective, speculative, and "authoritative" viewpoints. In this book the author is unable to go into any one of these subjects. However, one of the most useless arguments is over semantics. Therefore, before discussing the selection effect, the terminology that is to be adopted in this chapter must be defined and clarified. One word, especially a common word, can usually be used in many different senses. For want of new words, we shall also use the terms *selection*, *fitness*, and so on, but in a very restrictive and specialized sense, completely devoid of connotations of common usage. This is the difference between a technical term in science and a common word in everyday conversation, although they may happen to have the same spelling.

Consider the two alleles A and a of a certain locus, and suppose that 30 per cent of the genes are A and 70 per cent a at a given time in a population; ignore the small effects of mutation for the time being. If the frequency of A becomes 35 per cent and that of a 65 per cent in the next generation and if the change in gene frequency is due to differential multiplication or transmission of the two genes, then we say there is *selection*, in this case, favoring A and against a. Alternatively, we may say that the survival values of the two genes are different. Selection is entirely a figurative term. Also, when we say there is selection, it does not at all imply that we know how or why. In most cases, we do not have the slightest idea, even when the existence of selection has been proved by experimental procedure. The term selection, in this sense, can only be applied a posteriori, that is, after the differential survival has been observed. In other words, selection describes the differential multiplication or transmission of the genes, whatever the cause. When differential multiplication of the genes exists and yet there is no change in the final gene frequency, we say that the population is in *equilibrium* (with respect to selection).

Similarly, we may consider the three genotypes AA, Aa, aa. If each genotype contributes on the average the same number of living offspring to the next generation, we say there is no selection. Conversely, if for every 100 living children produced by AA or Aa, the genotype aa produces only 90, we say there is selection; or, alternatively, we say aa is less fit. When learning Chinese composition in elementary school, we are taught to say the same thing in different ways, such as:

"The tree is in front of the temple."

"The temple is behind the tree."

Analogously, we regard the following four statements as equivalent:

"Selection favors the dominants."

"Selection is against the recessives."

"Dominants have a greater fitness than recessives."

"Recessives are less fit than dominants."

The difference is in the subject of the sentences and not in their meaning. In this chapter selection and fitness are used only in this sense, referring to differential reproduction or differential contribution of genes to the offspring generation and to nothing else. Statements that amount to "These people are unfit and have too many children; they should be sterilized" are not uncommon. Whether one agrees with these viewpoints or not, it must be emphatically pointed out that the meaning of "fit" in these statements is entirely different from that of "fit" in selection genetics, defined in this chapter: they are as different as the cell of a plant in a prison cell is from the cell of a political party holding a meeting in the cell of a monastery. The author may have labored this point too long; if so, it is because he is confused by the voluminous essays in which selection, fitness, etc., have not been precisely defined. Perhaps the author is not the only one who feels that terminology should be clarified. Haldane (1949, p. 288), a pioneer in selection genetics, wrote:

> The fitness of a genotype in the Darwinian sense is measured by the mean number of its progeny, different generations being counted at the same stage of the life cycle . . . . If we are concerned with changes in the composition of a population, we need only consider the relative fitness of different genotypes. It is hardly necessary to emphasize that fitness throughout will be taken to mean fitness in this strictly Darwinian sense, and not fitness for football, industry, music, self-government, or any other activity.

For a lucid explanation of the meaning of fitness in human genetics the reader may consult Medawar (1959), and for a specific discussion see Reed (1959).

Direct Genic Selection: Balance between Mutation and Selection

To illustrate the principle of selection, let us first consider the case in which selection acts directly on genes (or gametes, if the reader prefers to think so). Suppose that the frequencies of A and a are p and $q = 1 - p$ at a certain time in a population and that the two genes multiply and transmit to the next generation in the ratio $1:1 - s$, where s is a positive fraction, being called the *selection coefficient* against gene a. Alternatively, $w = 1 - s$ is called the *fitness* of the gene. The gene frequencies will be in the ratio $p:q(1 - s)$ after one generation of selection. If this process continues for a large number of generations, all genes will be A; that is, a will be eliminated from the population. This unidirectional change leads to a dead end; when all genes are A or a, there will be no selection.

Since the gene frequencies p and q become $p:q(1 - s)$ after one generation of selection, totaling $p + q(1 - s) = 1 - sq$, the new frequencies are then:

$$p' = \frac{p}{1 - sq} \qquad q' = \frac{q(1 - s)}{1 - sq}$$

so $p' + q' = 1$. There is here no implication that the population is decreasing or increasing in size, because we are dealing merely with the relative frequencies of the two genes. To make this point perfectly clear, let $s = \frac{1}{3}$, so the reproduction rate (fitness) of the two genes are $1:\frac{2}{3}$, or $3:2$. Should the number of A genes be increased six times in the next generation, then the number of a genes would be *increased* four times, and so on, but the relative frequency of a in the entire body of genes will be decreased, as the following example shows:

Generation	Gene Number			Gene Frequency		
	A	a	Total	p	q	Total
1	100	150	250	.40	.60	1.00
2	600	600	1,200	.50	.50	1.00
3	1,800	1,200	3,000	.60	.40	1.00

The change in absolute size of a population is quite a different problem, and many ecologic factors are involved. Here, we are merely investigating the change due to selection in genetic composition *within* a population.

It has been pointed out that unidirectional change leads to a genetically uniform condition. Since selection is against gene a and yet there is still a small amount of gene a existing in our population, there must be some compensating mechanism by which gene a can maintain its existence. One may recall that all genes mutate at some finite rate per generation. If a certain proportion of A genes mutate to a in every generation, then the population will have a certain amount of gene a in spite of the selection against it. Now let us examine this situation in more detail. The amount of change in the frequency of gene a due to selection per generation is:

$$\Delta q = q' - q = \frac{q - sq}{1 - sq} - q = \frac{-spq}{1 - sq}$$

where the negative sign means that the frequency of a is decreasing. At the same time, however, a proportion μ of the A genes will mutate to a. The amount of new mutation is $\mu p' = \mu p/(1 - sq)$. When the loss due to selection is exactly balanced by the new additions from mutation, the equilibrium condition is obtained:

$$\frac{spq}{1 - sq} = \frac{\mu p}{1 - sq}$$

that is,

$$\mu = sq \quad \text{or} \quad q = \frac{\mu}{s}$$

For example, if $\mu = 6 \times 10^{-5}$ and $s = \frac{1}{3}$, the equilibrium value of the frequency of a will be:

$$q = \frac{6 \times 10^{-5}}{\frac{1}{3}} = .00018$$

When this condition is reached, there will be no change in gene frequency because eliminations due to selection and additions from mutation balance each other.

Since the equilibrium of the frequency of a is a small quantity (of the order of μ), $1 - sq$ is very nearly equal to unity. For most purposes the change in frequency due to selection may be written $\Delta q = -spq$. Note that this expression contains the factor pq, indicating that Δq is zero when $q = 0$ or 1; that is, when all genes are of one type, there is no selection.

Average Life Length of a Harmful Gene

The gene a in the previous section will be called the *harmful gene*. Since A and a multiply in the ratio $1:(1 - s)$, we may think of s as the probability that gene a will be eliminated in any one generation and $1 - s = w$ as the probability that the gene will survive to the next generation. After it survives one generation, it will face the same probabilities of elimination and survival in the next generation again. In other words, the probability of elimination or survival is purely a property of the gene and independent of time. Having survived a number of generations neither increases nor decreases the probability of elimination or survival in future generations. Hence, tracing the life of a newly mutated gene, we obtain the frequencies (probabilities) of elimination in successive generations shown in Table 9-1. In the first generation

TABLE 9-1. DISTRIBUTION OF ELIMINATION ("DEATH") OF
HARMFUL GENES*

Time, in generations t	Frequency of Elimination		
	General $f(t)$	$(s = .8000)$ $f(t)$	$(s = .3333)$ $f(t)$
1	s	0.80000	0.3333
2	ws	.16000	.2222
3	w^2s	.03200	.1481
4	w^3s	.00640	.0988
5	w^4s	.00128	.0658
6	w^5s	.00026	.0439
7	w^6s	.00005	.0293
8	w^7s	.00001	.0195
9	w^8s	....	.0130
10	w^9s	....	.0087
11	$w^{10}s$	....	.0058
12	$w^{11}s$	....	.0039
13	$w^{12}s$	....	.0026
14	$w^{13}s$	....	.0017
15	$w^{14}s$	....	.0011
16+	....	....	.0023
Total........	1.00	1.00000	1.0000
Mean........	$1/s$	1.25000	3.0000
Variance.....	w/s^2	0.31250	6.0000

* s = selection coefficient = probability of being eliminated in each generation; $w = 1 - s$ = probability of surviving one generation.

after the mutation occurs, a proportion s is eliminated and $1 - s = w$ survives. Of the latter, a proportion s is eliminated in the second generation, and so on. An elimination may be thought of as a "death" of the gene. The average length of life of a harmful gene (i.e., the number of generations it is expected to stay in the population) is:

$$\bar{t} = \Sigma t f(t) = \quad s + 2ws + 3w^2 s + 4w^3 s + \cdots$$
$$= s(1 + 2w \ + 3w^2 \ + 4w^3 \ + \cdots)$$
$$= s\left(\frac{1}{(1-w)^2}\right) = \frac{1}{s}$$

NOTE: When the time interval becomes increasingly short and s small, the limiting (continuous) distribution function becomes

$$f(t) = se^{-st}$$

with mean $1/s$ and variance $1/s^2$. It is sometimes used in finding the service life of certain manufactured products in industry and in estimating the survival of patients of certain chronic diseases. It is also the function that describes the rate of radioactive decay, from which the half-life is calculated. In words, the mean life of a harmful gene is equal to the reciprocal of the selection coefficient against that gene.

In our previous example s has been taken to be $\frac{1}{3}$. In order to shorten the arithmetic, an additional example with $s = .80$ has also been given in Table 9-1. The reader should calculate the mean for each distribution and convince himself that when $s = .80$, mean $= 1/.80 = 1.25$, and when $s = \frac{1}{3}$, mean $= 3$. These two numerical examples illustrate clearly the fact that a very harmful gene will be eliminated rapidly from the population (up to a low frequency supported by new mutations), whereas a mildly harmful gene will stay in the population for a long time.

With $\bar{t} = 1/s$, the equilibrium condition $q = \mu/s$, established in the last section, immediately acquires a very simple meaning. The situation is very similar to that of Muller's trucking company (Varying Service Life, Chap. 7). The new trucks bought each year are equivalent to new harmful mutations. The life length of a truck is the life length of the harmful gene. Each year a number of new trucks are added and the same number of old trucks are eliminated. Analogously, in each generation a number of new mutations are added to the population and the same number of mutations are eliminated from it. The equilibrium formulas in these two cases take the same form. Thus,

$$\begin{array}{ccc}
\text{Equilibrium number} & = & \text{number of new trucks} \\
\text{of trucks} & & \text{bought each year}
\end{array} \times \begin{array}{c}
\text{average life length} \\
\text{of truck}
\end{array}$$

$$\begin{array}{ccc}
\text{Equilibrium frequency} & = & \text{mutation rate of} \\
\text{of harmful genes} & & \text{harmful gene}
\end{array} \times \begin{array}{c}
\text{average life length} \\
\text{of harmful gene}
\end{array}$$

$$q \quad = \quad \mu \quad \times \quad \frac{1}{s}$$

The reader should again refer to Chap. 7 for details of the properties of this type of equilibrium. For a given mutation rate (buy two trucks each year), the equilibrium frequency of a slightly harmful gene with a long life length will be much higher than that of a very harmful gene with a short life length. (If a truck lasts on the average for 10 years, the company would have 20 trucks. If a truck has to be junked in 3 years, the company would have only 6.) This explains the fact that very severe hereditary defects in man are rare and mild anomalies are comparatively common.

Also, the reader may recall that the truck pictures (Figs. 7-3 and 7-4) can be read both ways—horizontally as well as vertically. In exactly the same manner, the distribution in Table 9-1 can be interpreted in two different ways. It has been regarded as the life history of a harmful gene. Alternatively, it may be regarded as the "age" distribution of existing harmful genes in an equilibrium population at any time. Thus, of all the harmful genes existing, for the case $s = \frac{1}{3}$, approximately 33 per cent are one generation old, 22 per cent are two generations old, 1.30 per cent are nine generations old, and so on. It is seen that most very harmful genes are comparatively new. On the other hand, most of the mildly harmful genes are old.

Finally, it is reiterated that the equilibrium $q = \mu/s$ is a stable one and is determined by "rules of game" only. If for any reason at all, the frequency of a is increased or decreased by agents other than natural mutation rate and selection coefficient, the disturbance is temporary and the frequency will come back to the same value μ/s after the disturbing agent is withdrawn. For a very harmful gene ($s = .80$, say), the comeback will be accomplished in a few generations. For a gene with $s = .08$, it may take hundreds.

It is contradictory to our definition of fitness and selection to say that a harmful gene may spread to the whole population, as some persons have implied. A harmful (less fit) gene is one that decreases in frequency. This definition is no different from many others in human society; as the Chinese historian says, "The victorious is called a king. The defeated, a bandit."

The simple case of genic selection has been discussed in detail for several reasons. First, all the important features of equilibrium between mutation and selection can be readily seen without mathematical juggling. Second, some types of genotypic selection, which will be discussed in the next few sections, either reduce to this case or bear a strong resemblance to it. Third, this simple case may be used as a "standard" with which other types of selection may be compared.

Unidirectional Selection of Genotypes

Now consider the three genotypes AA, Aa, aa, in a random-mating population, and let their fitness value be w_1, w_2, w_3, respectively. Again, since we are dealing with their relative reproductiveness or relative contribution of genes to the offspring generation, one of the three w's may be taken as 1.00, at least for calculation purposes, although this is not necessary in theoretical formulations. Some of the possible selection schemes are given in Table 9-2, in which the largest w is taken to be 1. This convention

TABLE 9-2. SIMPLE TYPES OF GENOTYPIC SELECTION WITHIN
A POPULATION

Genotype	Freq. f	Fitness w	Favor Aa w	Against Aa w	Against aa w	Against a w	Against A- w
AA	p^2	w_1	.80	.90	1.00	1.00	0
Aa	$2pq$	w_2	1.00	.70	1.00	.98	.60
aa	q^2	w_3	.70	1.00	.75	.96	1.00
Equilibrium..	......	$\bar{q}$	Stable	Unstable	To be balanced by mutation		

is, however, by no means universal. Some investigators take the

w of the most frequent genotype in a population as 1, the "standard."

It is convenient to consider first the *unidirectional* (or *monotonic*) cases in which $w_1 > w_2 > w_3$ or $w_1 < w_2 < w_3$. One of the inequality signs may be replaced by an equality sign, as exemplified in the last three columns of Table 9-2. These cases constitute a natural continuation of the case treated in the preceding two sections. Obviously, this type of selection tends to reduce the frequency of a to zero or to raise it to unity if unopposed by new mutations. Hence, selection and its balance by mutation may be considered simultaneously.

In the upper part of Table 9-3 is given the general procedure of calculating the new gene frequency after one generation of selection. It deserves a few minutes of careful study before we proceed to any particular case. The genotype frequencies before selection are in Hardy-Weinberg proportions due to random mating, and those after selection are determined by fitness values. The total of the latter is denoted by $\bar{w}$, because it can be thought of as the average value of the three w's in the population. The new gene frequency after selection is the frequency of homozygotes plus half that of heterozygotes, divided by the total $\bar{w}$, so $p' + q' = 1$. The amount of change in the frequency of a in one generation of selection is $\Delta q = q' - q$. On random union of the selected gametes, that is, expanding $(p' + q')^2$, we obtain the genotype proportions of the next generation prior to selection, thus completing a cycle.

Now we are ready to consider a specific $w_1 > w_2 > w_3$ type of selection, viz., 1, $(1 - s)$, $(1 - s)^2$, as shown in the middle portion of Table 9-3. This set of fitness values means that if Aa is, for instance, 5 per cent less fit than AA, then aa is 5 per cent less fit than Aa. Proceeding according to the general procedure and simplifying the algebraic expressions, we obtain the new gene frequencies as shown in the table. Note that these expressions are identical with those obtained by genic selection on p. 147. It follows that the amount of change in gene frequency per generation (Δq) is also the same. The conclusion is that this type of genotypic selection is equivalent to genic selection. The equilibrium condition must be also the same, i.e., $q = \mu/s$.

In the numerical example on genic selection (p. 147), we have

TABLE 9-3. SELECTION OF GENOTYPES IN A PANMICTIC POPULATION: GENERAL PROCEDURE

Genotype	Fitness w	Before selection f	After selection fw	New gene frequency
AA	w_1	p^2	p^2w_1	$p' = \dfrac{p^2w_1 + pqw_2}{\bar{w}}$
Aa	w_2	$2pq$	$2pqw_2$	
aa	w_s	q^2	q^2w_3	$q' = \dfrac{q^2w_3 + pqw_2}{\bar{w}}$
Total......	....	1.00	$\bar{w}$	1.00

Fitness value decreases in proportion

AA	1	p^2	p^2	$p' = \dfrac{p}{1 - sq}$
Aa	$1 - s$	$2pq$	$2pq(1 - s)$	
aa	$(1 - s)^2$	q^2	$q^2(1 - s)^2$	$q' = \dfrac{q(1 - s)}{1 - sq}$
Total......	....	1.00	$(1 - sq)^2$	1.00

Numerical example ($s = \frac{1}{3}$ and $p = q = \frac{1}{2}$)

AA	1	.2500	.2500	$p' = \dfrac{.4167}{.6944} = .60$
Aa	$\frac{2}{3}$	.5000	.3333	
aa	$\frac{4}{9}$	.2500	.1111	$q' = \dfrac{.2778}{.6944} = .40$
Total......	....	1.0000	.6944	1.00

seen that when $s = \frac{1}{3}$, the frequency of a decreases from .50 to .40 in one generation. The lower portion of Table 9-3 verifies that this is also the case with genotypic selection.

When s is small, s^2 will be negligible; the three fitness values may then be taken as:

$$w = 1 \quad 1 - s \quad 1 - 2s \quad \text{with } \bar{w} = 1 - 2sq$$

e.g., when $s = .02$, $\quad w = 1 \quad\quad .98 \quad\quad .96$

Hence, for mild selections and when the fitness of the heterozygote is in between that of the homozygotes, the selection of genotypes is equivalent to direct selection of genes. Loci affecting quantitative traits could be of this nature, each allele having a small effect but no dominance. Therefore, the equilibrium condition between mutation and selection,

$$q = \mu/s$$

may be applicable to a large number of cases in nature. Other interesting properties of this type of selection have been given by Li (1959).

Selection against Recessives

Three other cases of unidirectional selection against recessives will be dealt with very briefly, not because they are less important in human populations, but because the results can all be easily worked out by the general procedure given in Table 9-3. One case is selection against recessives only; the heterozygote suffers no defect to impair reproductiveness. (The reader must consult other textbooks for the many examples and good pictures of recessive hereditary diseases.) Letting $w_1 = w_2 = 1$ and $w_3 = 1 - s$, we obtain:

$$\bar{w} = 1 - sq^2 \qquad q' = \frac{q - sq^2}{\bar{w}} \qquad \Delta q = q' - q = -\frac{spq^2}{\bar{w}}$$

The latter must be balanced by new mutations from A to a in an equilibrium population. The amount of such mutation is $\mu p' = \mu p/\bar{w}$. Equating the loss due to selection and the gain through mutation, we obtain the equilibrium condition:

$$\mu = sq^2 \quad \text{or} \quad q^2 = \mu/s$$

This equilibrium formula has the same form as the one for genic selection except that q^2 takes the place of q. In genic selection, q is the frequency of a and s is selection coefficient against gene a. Here, q^2 is the frequency of aa and s is selection coefficient against genotype aa. When $\mu = 6 \times 10^{-5}$ and $s = \frac{1}{3}$, the equilibrium proportion of recessive individuals will be $q^2 = .00018$. The recessive gene frequency is, however, much higher, being:

$$q = \sqrt{\mu/s} = \sqrt{.00018} = .0134$$

This is, of course, readily understandable. When the frequency of a is low in a population, most recessive genes are hidden in heterozygotes and only a few recessive homozygotes are exposed to selection effect. The equilibrium composition of the population is approximately:

AA	Aa	aa	Total
.97335	.02647	.00018	1.00000

In each generation, $sq^2 = \mu$ recessives will be eliminated by selection and an equal amount added from segregation of old and new mutations. It is rather expected that a human population has a large number of recessive deleterious loci. (So do all other natural populations.) Selection is comparatively ineffective against the recessive gene. The primary effect is on the frequency of aa, which is reduced to a low level of the order of mutation rate.

The second case is the most severe possible form of selection against the recessives. If the recessive disease exhibited by genotype aa is *lethal* (not necessarily fatal but causing inability to have children), then $w_3 = 0$, and substituting $s = 1$ in the formulas of the previous case, we obtain:

$$q' = \frac{q}{1 + q}$$

This is the *sequence equation* of a harmonic series. If q_0 is the initial gene frequency, then after one generation of selection, $q_1 = q_0/(1 + q_0)$, and after two generations,

$$q_2 = \frac{q_1}{1 + q_1} = \frac{q_0}{1 + 2q_0}$$

and so on. Successive substitution shows that after n generations of complete elimination of recessives, the gene frequency will be reduced to:

$$q_n = \frac{q_0}{1 + nq_0}$$

If $nq_0 = 1$, $q_n = \frac{1}{2}q_0$. In words, $n = 1/q_0$ generations of complete elimination of recessive individuals will reduce the frequency of a to half its original value. Suppose that at the present time the frequency of a certain recessive deleterious gene is $q_0 = .0050$ and a vigorous eugenic program is enforced so that every aa individual is sterilized in every generation. To reduce $q_0 = .0050$ to $q_n = .0025$, we need to enforce the program for

$$n = \frac{1}{q_0} = \frac{1}{.005} = 200 \text{ generations}$$

or approximately six thousand years! Actually, the eugenic accomplishment will be much less than indicated, because mutations from A to a have been ignored in the calculation. Again, substituting $s = 1$ in our previous equilibrium formula, we obtain the equilibrium condition:

$$q^2 = \mu \quad \text{or} \quad q = \sqrt{\mu}$$

If $\mu = .000009$, the equilibrium of the frequency of a is $q = .0030$. Continuous elimination of recessives will maintain the frequency of a at this level, and probably the lower level of $q = .0025$ will never be reached. It is clear that we can only hope to reduce the frequency of a to a minimum level; we can never get rid of the harmful gene completely.

The third case is where the so-called recessive trait is not entirely recessive in nature. The heterozygote may have a fitness slightly below that of homozygous dominants. The three fitness values may thus be something like $1:.98:.70$. Writing $1:1 - s: 1 - (2 + k)s$, where $s = .02$ and $k = 13$ in the numerical example, and proceeding exactly as before, we obtain the equilibrium condition shown in the following. It is given together with the results of previous cases for comparison:

	w_1	w_2	w_3	Equilibrium condition
No dominance	1	$1 - s$	$1 - 2s$	$\mu = sq$
Full dominance	1	1	$1 - s$	$\mu = sq^2$
Partial dominance	1	$1 - s$	$1 - (2 + k)s$	$\mu = sq + ksq^2$

It is seen that the last equilibrium condition is intermediate between those with full and those with no dominance.

Unidirectional Selection against Dominant Phenotypes

Unidirectional selection is much more effective against dominant phenotypes than against recessives. Again, the change in gene frequency may be worked out by using the general procedure given in Table 9-3. Equating the amount of change with the amount of new mutations, we obtain the equilibrium condition. Here, it is $p = \text{freq}(A)$ that is reduced to a very small value, and we need only to consider the mutations from a to A at the rate ν per generation. Some of the results may be obtained simply by replacing q by p and μ by ν in the formulas for selection against the recessives.

Perhaps a word of caution about terminology will help clarify the situation. Consider, for example, the *trait* brachydactyly in man. It is due to a dominant gene, so Aa has short fingers and aa is normal. However, the brachydactylous individuals have normal fitness, and the selection is against the homozygous dominants only. In this particular case, AA is probably lethal, so all brachydactylous individuals are heterozygotes. Hence, with respect to fingers, A is dominant; with respect to selection, A is actually recessive. The three fitness values may be written as $(w_1, w_2, w_3) = (1 - s, 1, 1)$ in general and $(0, 1, 1)$ when AA is lethal. Thus, this case is entirely analogous to selection against recessives. Hence, the equilibrium condition is in general $\nu = sp^2$ and when $s = 1$ and $w_1 = 0$, $p = \sqrt{\nu}$.

If AA is lethal, the heterozygote may have a lower fitness $(1 - s)$ than the normal aa. In this case, the selection is again equivalent to direct selection against the genes, and thus the equilibrium condition is $p = \nu/s$. Finally, there are cases in which all individuals with the dominant gene are so severely diseased that they do not live to reproduce at all. In such an extreme case, it is obvious that all dominant genes are new mutations, and hence $p = \nu$.

Since the dominant heterozygous individuals are distinguishable (whereas this is impossible for recessive traits), the equilibrium conditions stated above may also be expressed in terms of incidence of the disease (i.e., proportion of heterozygotes, $H = 2pq \doteq 2p$) in the population. The results may be summarized as follows:

Example	w_1	w_2	w_3	$Freq(A)$	Heterozygote proportion	Mutation rate
Brachydactyly	0	1	1	$p = \sqrt{\nu}$	$H = 2\sqrt{\nu}$	$\nu = \frac{1}{4}H^2$
Achondroplasia	0	$1 - s$	1	$p = \nu/s$	$H = 2\nu/s$	$\nu = \frac{1}{2}Hs$
Retinoblastoma	0	0	1	$p = \nu$	$H = 2\nu$	$\nu = \frac{1}{2}H$

Gross chromosomal aberrations in man behave like a dominant lethal gene. Lejeune et al. (1959a, b) discovered that mongoloid imbeciles have an extra small acrocentric chromosome, being *trisomic* for chromosome number 21. This finding was immediately confirmed by Ford and his associates and, soon after, by several others. For a review and bibliography on mongoloid and sex chromosomal aberrations, the reader is referred to Ford (1960). Mongoloids have a very high death rate, especially in early ages, and in general do not have children (genetically lethal). There are only two or three known cases of female mongoloids having offspring. For all practical purposes, the situation is similar to the selection scheme (0, 0, 1) for dominant lethals shown above. In other words, all mongoloids are new in each generation, arisen from fresh nondisjunction at meiosis. If the frequency of mongoloid at birth is approximately $H = \frac{1}{660}$, then the rate of nondisjunction for the pair of autosomes under consideration should be approximately $\nu = p = \frac{1}{2}H = 1/1{,}320$. However, in view of the well-known maternal age effect in the case of mongoloids, it is probable that nondisjunction occurs more frequently at oogenesis than at spermatogenesis. In such an event the estimated $\nu = 1/1,320$ is the average rate for both sexes. In the extreme case that all nondisjunction occurs in females, i.e., $\nu_f = \frac{1}{660}$ and $\nu_m = 0$, the average is still $\nu = 1/1,320$. The frequency of nondisjunction for sex chromosomes may be estimated in a similar way.

Genetic Polymorphism and Selectional Balance

Unidirectional selection, as we have seen, invariably reduces the frequency of harmful gene to a very low level and would eliminate it from the population, were it not for the new mutations that arise in each generation. Although the harmful gene is still present in the population, it is not regarded as a phenomenon of *polymorphism*. By true polymorphism it is meant that two or more alleles coexist in a population with intermediate frequencies that are too high to be explained by new mutations. The MN and ABO alleles are familiar examples of genetic polymorphism. There must be compensating mechanisms other than mutation supporting these alleles so the population can attain an equilibrium state. In the absence of selection, the gene frequencies will remain unchanged from generation to generation (Chap. 2). Therefore, one explanation of polymorphism is that all genotypes are of the same fitness, at least at the present time. The origin of polymorphism—the mechanism by which polymorphism came into existence in the first place—is another question and remains unknown.

However, under certain conditions, selection force alone can maintain polymorphism in equilibrium. To show this, let us return once more to the general procedure outlined in Table 9-3. The new gene frequency after one generation of selection is q', and the amount of change is $\Delta q = q' - q$. If $q' = q$, so there is no change in gene frequency between successive generations, the population is then in equilibrium, the condition being:

$$q = q' = \frac{q^2 w_3 + pq\, w_2}{p^2 w_1 + 2pq\, w_2 + q^2 w_3}$$

Solving by a few steps of algebra, we obtain:

$$q = \frac{w_2 - w_1}{(w_2 - w_1) + (w_2 - w_3)}$$

In order that q be a positive fraction, $(w_2 - w_1)$ and $(w_2 - w_3)$ must be (1) both positive or (2) both negative. In other words, the fitness of heterozygote must be (1) the greatest or (2) the smallest:

$$(1) \quad w_1 < w_2 > w_3 \qquad (2) \quad w_1 > w_2 < w_3$$

An example of each has been given in the middle columns of Table 9-2.

Case 1 is far more important than Case 2 for reasons that will be made clear shortly. Let us consider the numerical example of Case 1 listed in Table 9-2. Since w_2 is the greatest, it may be taken as unity; thus,

$$\left. \begin{array}{l} w_1 = 1 - s_1 = \ .80 \\ w_2 = 1 \qquad\ \ \ = 1.00 \\ w_3 = 1 - s_3 = \ .70 \end{array} \right\} \qquad \begin{array}{l} w_2 - w_1 = s_1 = .20 \\ \\ w_2 - w_3 = s_3 = .30 \end{array}$$

Under this scheme of selection, neither gene A nor gene a will be eliminated because Aa has the greatest fitness. Consequently, both genes will be maintained in the population. This is the chief difference between this type of selection and the unidirectional. The equilibrium condition in this example is, according to the general formula at the bottom of p. 160,

$$q = \frac{s_1}{s_1 + s_3} = \frac{.20}{.20 + .30} = .40$$

Table 9-4 gives the numerical details to show that the population with $q = .40$ is actually in equilibrium under the specified scheme of selection. The loss of AA and aa is so balanced by the gain of Aa that there is no change in gene frequency. Since this type of genetic equilibrium is entirely due to the operation of selection, it may be called *selectional balance*, to be distinguished from the balance by mutation. This equilibrium is stable.

Probably the most conspicuous example of selectional balance in man is the greater resistance to falciparum malaria of the sickling heterozygote (Allison, 1954a and b, and later). The incidence of sickle cell trait (AS, see Chap. 4) in certain African populations is extraordinarily high, in spite of the fact that sickle cell anemia patients (SS) die young and seldom have children. As an illustration, the extreme situation of the Baamba popula-

TABLE 9-4. SELECTIONAL BALANCE WHEN THE HETEROZYGOTE HAS
THE GREATEST FITNESS

Genotype	Fitness w	Frequency before selection f	Frequency after selection fw	New gene frequency $q = q'$	Genotypic proportion in next generation $f = f'$
AA	.80	.36	.288		.36
Aa	1.00	.48	.480	$p = \dfrac{.528}{.880} = .60$	.48
aa	.70	.16	.112	$q = \dfrac{.352}{.880} = .40$	.16
Total..	....	1.00	0.880	1.00	1.00

An example in man: Baamba population in Africa

Genotype	Fitness	Observed adults (after selection)	Gene frequency	Next Generation	
				Births	Adults
AA	$1 - s$	.60		.64	.64(1 − s)
AS	1	.40	$p = .80$	.32	.32
SS	0	0	$q = .20$	.04	0
Total..	.....	1.00	1.00	1.00	.96 − .64s

tion in Africa is given in the lower part of Table 9-4, in which it is
assumed that $w_3 = 0$ and $w_1 = 1 - s$, because there are presumably more deaths from malaria among the AA individuals than
among heterozygous persons. It is found that 39 per cent of the
adults have sickle cell trait, and it is taken to be 40 per cent for
easy calculation. The problem is to estimate the value of w_1 or s
that would maintain such a population in equilibrium. Proceeding
as indicated in the table, we see that the equilibrium condition is:

$$\frac{.32}{.96 - .64\,s} = .40 \quad \text{or} \quad s = .25$$

In other words, the set of fitness values (.75, 1.00, 0) will maintain a selectional balance with $q = .20$ and 40 per cent heterozygous persons among the selected adults. Mutation plays very little role in this type of equilibrium, because the selection coefficients are so many times larger than the mutation rates.

The Baamba example is cited here purely for the purposes of illustrating selectional balance and the method of estimating s from observed data; it does not imply that no other selectional mechanisms may also be involved in the sickle hemoglobin locus. The model presented above requires an enormous number of malaria deaths among the "normal" (AA) individuals, and some investigators wonder if this is the case. Lehmann and Raper (1956) think that the malaria toll occurs *after* the nonselective causes of death have taken their toll.

Unstable Equilibrium

Case 2, in which w_2 is the lowest of the three fitness values, presents an entirely different situation. Returning to the example given in Table 9-2 $(w_1:w_2:w_3 = .90:.70:1.00)$ and the general formula for selectional balance, we find the equilibrium gene frequency:

$$q = \frac{w_2 - w_1}{(w_2 - w_1) + (w_2 - w_3)} = \frac{-.20}{-.20 - .30} = .40$$

The equilibrium value is the same as that in Case 1 but has a different property. The reader should verify the following three results as exercises on problems in selection genetics:

If $q = .40$, it remains the same in the next generation.

If $q = .80$, it increases to .836 in the next generation.

If $q = .20$, it decreases to .181 in the next generation.

Further calculation shows that if $q > .40$, it will continue to increase, and if $q < .40$, it will continue to decrease in later generations. In other words, the q value moves away from the equilibrium value .40, which is thus said to be unstable. This situation is very similar to the unstable equilibrium described in Chap. 7 under Equal Contribution and Matching. In short, equal contribution hurts the poor fellow more than the rich, making the poor poorer and the rich richer, relatively. The equal contribution in that story is equivalent to selection against heterozygotes here, for each death of an Aa individual eliminates one A gene as well as one a gene. Hence, selection of this type makes the lower gene frequency still lower and the higher frequency still higher in later generations. A slight deviation from the precarious condition ($q = .40$ in the example) is sufficient to throw it off balance, so to speak, and make q either decrease to zero or increase to unity. An unstable equilibrium is not expected to exist in natural populations. If it existed, it would be near to $q = 1$ or 0 by now, the low frequency being supported by mutations.

An example of selection against heterozygotes in man is the "Rh baby" (erythroblastosis fetalis) and probably also some other types of blood incompatibility. The Rh baby is an Rh-positive child from an Rh-negative mother and is therefore always heterozygous. In our language, AA and aa are normal, but Aa has a lower fitness. In all the preceding sections it is assumed that the w's are constants. In the case of the Rh baby, however, w_2 is not a constant but varies with gene frequency of the population. That this is so should be at once clear when one remembers that the blood disease is not an inherent defect of the heterozygous individual but is due to the particular mother-child combination, the incidence of which depends on gene frequency. Space does not permit further discussion here; some details about the problem have been given by Glass (1950), Li (1953a), and Lewontin (1953). It suffices to say that, at the present stage of our knowledge, the fate of the Rh locus is still a great puzzle to human geneticists: evidence from selection shows that it is an unstable situation, and yet the frequency of the Rh gene remains fairly high in most Western populations (Race and Sanger, 1954, p. 122).

This is no place to go into details of equilibrium mathematics involving second derivatives. Nevertheless, the reader may wonder how one can tell that a given equilibrium is stable or unstable. One sure way to find out is to try a series of q values in the neighborhood of the equilibrium value (say, $\bar{q}$) and see if they become closer to $\bar{q}$ (stable) in the following generation or become further apart from $\bar{q}$ (unstable). For simple cases in which there are three genotypes and their fitness values are constants, the stability of an equilibrium may be seen by ploting the curve (Fig. 9-1):

$$\bar{w} = p^2 w_1 + 2pq\,w_2 + q^2 w_3$$

If the curve has a maximum, the equilibrium is stable and $\bar{q}$ is the point at which $\bar{w}$ is greatest. If the curve has a minimum, the equilibrium is unstable and $\bar{q}$ is the point at which $\bar{w}$ is lowest. In brief, selection tends to maximize the value of $\bar{w}$ of a population

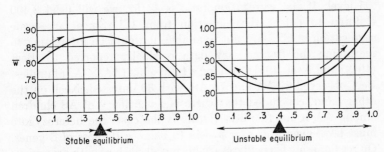

Stable equilibrium   Unstable equilibrium

FIG. 9-1. The stability of selectional equilibrium (from Li, 1955b):

$w_1:w_2:w_3 = .80:1.00:.70$
$\bar{w} = .80p^2 + 2pq + .70q^2$
$\quad = .80 + .40q - .50q^2$
which has a maximum at $q = .40$.

$w_1:w_2:w_3 = .90:.70:1.00$
$\bar{w} = .90p^2 + .70 \times 2pq + q^2$
$\quad = .90 - .40q + .50q^2$
which has a minimum at $q = .40$.

under a given scheme of genotypic selection. Several other and slightly more complicated situations have also been investigated by Levene (1953), Li (1955b), and Lewontin (1958).

Selection through Segregation

The investigation of human segregation (Chap. 5) in general is difficult for many reasons. Consequently, the segregation of most human genes is not accurately known, except that it conforms by and large with Mendelism. When all three genotypes are distinguishable (such as AA, AS, SS), the study of segregation should be comparatively easy; but there is very little actual investigation of this kind, because normal segregation has been more often taken for granted than taken as a matter for study. (Maybe it is considered too old-fashioned to study ratios.) This subject is brought up here because a slight deviation from the "normal" ratio will have a profound effect on gene frequency and equilibrium condition. For example, if an AS individual produces more S gametes than A (which amounts to gametic or genic selection), it will change considerably our estimate of the greater reproductive fitness of AS in African populations. Suppose that AA × AS on the average produce 45 per cent AA and 55 per cent AS offspring. We will need at least 384, or approximately 400, children to establish the deviation from 1:1 significantly at the .05 level. If the segregation ratio is 48:52, we will need 2,400 children to detect the deviation from 1:1. Since large-scale segregation studies are not available, it would be interesting to reexamine the fragmentary data originally reported by Beet (1949) and Neel (1951). Among a total of 32 (AA × AS) families, Beet observed 61 AA and 76 AS, with 30 untested. Neel, on the other hand, concluded that there is a deficiency of AS children among AA × AS families. If this is the case, the heterozygote must have even a greater fitness to balance the loss of S genes. On reexamining his pedigrees, ignoring all sibships with propositus and counting only the sibships identified through the parents, the author counted 14 AA and 18 AS children, with 4 untested. The evidence for more AS children is weak; the evidence for less AS children is nil.

Abnormal segregation in mice has been studied and its possible existence in man has been mentioned by Dunn (1953) and Prout (1953). Suppose that AS individuals produce $1 - m(A)$ and $m(S)$ gametes, where m is a positive fraction presumably greater than $\frac{1}{2}$. Still assuming greater fitness for the heterozygote and proceeding the same way as before (details in Table 9-5), we obtain the equilibrium condition:

$$\bar{q} = \frac{s_1 + 2m - 1}{s_1 + s_3}$$

Note that if $m = \frac{1}{2}$, the expression becomes $q = s_1/(s_1 + s_3)$ on p. 161. In the Baamba population, $w_3 = 0$, so $s_3 = 1$ and $\bar{q} = .20$. If $m = .55$, substituting and solving, we obtain:

$$s_1 = .125 \quad \text{and} \quad w_1 = 1 - s_1 = .875$$

Previously we have obtained $s_1 = .250$ with $m = \frac{1}{2}$. Thus, it is

TABLE 9-5. GREATER FITNESS AND UNEQUAL SEGREGATION
OF HETEROZYGOTES

Genotype	At birth f	Fitness w	Adults fw	Gametes produced	
				A	S
AA	p^2	$1 - s_1$	$p^2(1 - s_1)$	$p^2(1 - s_1)$	0
AS	$2pq$	1	$2pq$	$2pq(1 - m)$	$2pqm$
SS	q^2	$1 - s_3$	$q^2(1 - s_3)$	0	$q^2(1 - s_3)$
Total....	1.00	$\bar{w} = 1 - s_1 p^2 - s_3 q^2$		$g(\text{A})$	$g(\text{S})$

New gene frequency in the next generation: $p' = \dfrac{g(\text{A})}{\bar{w}} \qquad q' = \dfrac{g(\text{S})}{\bar{w}}$

Amount of change: $\qquad \Delta q = q' - q = \dfrac{pq}{\bar{w}}(2m - 1 + s_1 p - s_3 q)$

Equilibrium conditon ($\Delta q = 0$): $\qquad \bar{q} = \dfrac{s_1 + 2m - 1}{s_1 + s_3}$

Restriction:

$$0 < s_1 + 2m - 1 < s_1 + s_3 \quad \text{or} \quad \tfrac{1}{2}(1 - s_1) < m < \tfrac{1}{2}(1 + s_3)$$

seen that, should there be a slight deviation from normal segregation, excessive fitness of heterozygotes or large number of additional malaria deaths among AA individuals may not be necessary to maintain polymorphism in the AS locus. The purpose of this section is to stress the importance of segregation in determining equilibrium and the need for research on this point (Lewis and Li, 1958).

Miscellaneous Cases

There are numerous other schemes of selection that may operate in man. In closing, the author has a few comments about some of them and other related topics.

1. Selection may operate with different intensity in the two sexes. For autosomal genes, half of which are in females and half in males, selection coefficient s_f in females and s_m in males is equivalent to a selection coefficient $s = \frac{1}{2}(s_f + s_m)$ for both sexes. In particular, if one (say, s_f) is zero, the effect is the same

as $s = \frac{1}{2} s_m$ for the whole population. Under very special conditions, such as $w_1 < w_2 > w_3$ in one sex and $w_1 > w_2 < w_3$ in the other, two distinct stable equilibria are possible, and the population will be stabilized at one of them (Owen, 1953). More generally, if different selection schemes are operating in different localities or communities that interbreed, there could be a number of distinct stable equilibrium conditions (Levene, 1953; Li, 1955b). No example of either type is yet known in man. If selection and mutations of both directions are considered, there also could be two distinct stable equilibria.

2. For sex-linked genes, two-thirds of which are in females and one-third in males, the principle of averaging the selection coefficients s_f and s_m still applies with weight $\frac{2}{3}$ for s_f and $\frac{1}{3}$ for s_m. If $s_f = 0$, selection in males only is equivalent to selection with one-third intensity for the whole population. Take for example the selection coefficient s against the hemophilia gene in males. For genic selection in the entire population, the equilibrium condition is $\mu = sq$. When s applies only to males, the equilibrium condition is:

$$\mu = \frac{1}{3} sq$$

This may be seen from another viewpoint. In each generation, sq of the hemophilia genes are eliminated from the males which contain one-third of the total X-chromosomes, and the same amount must be replaced by mutations occurring on all the X-chromosomes at the rate μ. Hence, $3\mu = sq$. If mutation rates are different in the two sexes, μ_f in females and μ_m in males, the equilibrium condition will be $2\mu_f + \mu_m = sq$.

3. Estimation of mutation rates in man is based on the equilibrium conditions described under Unidirectional Selection of Genotypes, Selection against Recessives, and Unidirectional Selection against Dominant Phenotypes and not on direct observation. The equilibrium conditions are expressed in terms of μ or ν, s, and q or p. Hence, if selection coefficient and gene frequency can be approximately determined from observations, then the mutation rate may be calculated. Thus, if $\mu = sq^2$ is the equilibrium condition for a certain recessive deleterious trait, the value of s and q^2 must be determined first in order to calculate μ.

It may sound like a very simple problem, but this is not the case. In the first place, q^2 is a small quantity, not much larger than μ, and can seldom be determined with any accuracy. Second, the value of s has practically never been determined by any systematic methods, and in many cases it is assigned by the investigator. Assigning a value to s is almost equivalent to assigning a value to μ. Crow (1958) discusses some possibilities of measuring selection intensity in man. Finally, if q^2 and s are each determined with a certain error, their product, μ, will have a much greater error than either of them. A number of mutation rates in man have been estimated. These results are not reproduced here, not because they are not the best estimates available, but lest some readers might take them the way they take the table of atomic weights. This is certainly not the intention of investigators who make the estimates.

4. The threat of decline in intelligence level of man has been a frequent subject of discussion in various professional circles (anthropologists, biologists, demographers, educationists, sociologists, etc.). Even a very sketchy account of this problem is beyond the scope of this book. The reader is referred to Penrose (1954) for a general review and evaluation of the situation and is urged to read at least chap. VI, if not the whole book. Here we can only mention a few points that are directly connected with the subject matter of this chapter, viz., selection and equilibrium. Intelligence is supposed to be to a substantial extent controlled by genes; the higher intelligence group apparently reproduces less than the mediocre group, and hence the theory of decline of intelligence in man. (If this were true, we would not have enough intelligence left to be aware of the existence of such a problem, let alone to study it.) In addition to false premises and biased collection of data, a major defect of the theory of decline is the total disregard of the fact that the very low intelligence group also reproduces less, much less, than ordinary persons. Differential reproductivity with respect to intelligence may have prevailed for a long time in human history. When the lower reproductivity of both the high and the low intelligence groups is taken into consideration, we see immediately the possibility of equilibrium—indeed, a stable one resembling the polymorphism situation: $w_1 < w_2 > w_3$.

5. Just as two or more loci may be involved in determining the phenotype (Chap. 8, Epistasis), two or more loci may be involved in determining the fitness of an individual. Indeed, the interaction between loci in determining fitness may be more complicated and subtle than epistasis in determining phenotypes. As an example of two-loci interaction, Levine's (1943) discovery that ABO in-compatibility nullifies or lessens Rh incompatibility may be cited. Let D and d be the Rh-positive and -negative genes. If mother is O,dd and father is AB,DD, there will be no erythroblastotic child, although he is Rh positive. If the father is AO and the child is O, being compatible with the mother, the protection against erythro-blastosis will be lessened. The explanation is that the ABO-incom-patible fetal red cells are destroyed in the maternal circulation before they can immunize the mother against the D antigen. Once sensitization has occurred, ABO incompatibility is no longer protective. These findings have been subsequently confirmed by many workers. For instance, Clarke et al. (1958) found that, in 91 cases of erythroblastosis, ABO-incompatible families (mother O × father A) are much less frequent than ABO-compatible (mother A × father O) families. Before this discovery, one would think that these two incompatible systems either work independ-ently or enhance each other. But here we have an interaction by which one incompatible system nullifies the other, the total selection effect being less than the sum of the two separately. Generally speaking, if there is interaction between loci in deter-mining fitness, there will be a two-loci equilibrium, determined by the fitness of two-loci genotypes and gene frequencies. Thus, an equilibrium in human populations cannot always be explained on a monofactorial basis.

Chapter 10

Inbreeding and Cousin Marriages

Inbreeding is mating between genetically related individuals. The only important form of inbreeding in man that occurs with any appreciable frequency is first cousin marriages. Before studying the specific effects of (first) cousin marriages, it may be well to introduce briefly a general concept of inbreeding.

Correlation between Uniting Gametes

One of the reasons that association and incidence was discussed in some detail in Chap. 6 is that there is a formal analogy between that subject and inbreeding, the correspondence being as follows:

Contingency	*Genetics*
Incidence (marginal)	Gene frequency
Independence	Random mating
Association	Inbreeding
Correlation coefficient	Inbreeding coefficient

This correspondence is at once clear when the incidence of arthritis among the husbands and wives (p. 84) is replaced by the frequency of A genes or gametes in the two sexes. Thus, the genotypes in a random-mating population may be written as follows:

	A	a	
A	p^2	pq	p
a	pq	q^2	q
	p	q	1

	A	a	
A	.16	.24	.40
a	.24	.36	.60
	.40	.60	1.00

	A	a	
A	.49	.21	.70
a	.21	.09	.30
	.70	.30	1.00

Alternatively, we may say that there is no association or correlation between the uniting gametes (Fig. 2-1). When a person mates with his relative, there is a probability that they share a common gene identical by descent (Chap. 3); therefore the probability that the offspring will be homozygous is greater than p^2 and q^2 as dictated by chance, and the probability that he will be heterozygous is correspondingly less. The gene frequencies remain the same (the number of black and white gloves are fixed no matter how they are distributed among the members), with or without inbreeding. Thus, the inbreeding situation may be represented as follows, where ϵ is a positive fraction.

	A	a			A	a			A	a	
A	$p^2 + \epsilon$	$pq - \epsilon$	p		.175	.225	.40		.19	.21	.40
a	$pq - \epsilon$	$q^2 + \epsilon$	q		.225	.375	.60		.21	.39	.60
	p	q	1		.400	.600	1.00		.40	.60	1.00

The two numerical examples above stress the fact that the two populations have the same gene frequency but different degrees of inbreeding or association between the uniting gametes. The correlation coefficient for the numerical tables may be calculated in any manner the reader wishes, and he will find that it is $\frac{1}{16}$ for the first example and $\frac{1}{8}$ for the second. In the general case, assigning A the value 1 and a the value 0, we find that the correlation coefficient is (also see bottom of p. 83):

$$F = \frac{\epsilon}{pq} \quad \text{or} \quad \epsilon = Fpq$$

The reader may verify the formulas by numerical examples. One convenient way to describe the degree of inbreeding is to use the correlation coefficient F between the uniting gametes shown above. Thus, F is defined as the *inbreeding coefficient* of the population under consideration (Wright, 1921; see Wright, 1951). The genotypic proportions in a population with inbreeding are given in Table 10-1. When the correlation between uniting gametes is F, the proportions for homozygotes are each increased by an amount Fpq and those for heterozygotes decreased by $2Fpq$.

TABLE 10-1. GENOTYPIC PROPORTIONS IN A POPULATION WITH INBREEDING

Genotype	Frequency	$p = .40, q = .60, and F = \frac{1}{16}$
AA	$p^2 + Fpq = (1 - F)p^2 + Fp$	$.160 + .015 = .175$
Aa	$2pq - 2Fpq = 2(1 - F)pq$	$.480 - .030 = .450$
aa	$q^2 + Fpq = (1 - F)q^2 + Fq$	$.360 + .015 = .375$

Genotypic proportions for three alleles

	A_1	A_2	A_3	
A_1	$(1 - F)p^2 + Fp$	$(1 - F)pq$	$(1 - F)pr$	p
A_2	$(1 - F)pq$	$(1 - F)q^2 + Fq$	$(1 - F)qr$	q
A_3	$(1 - F)pr$	$(1 - F)qr$	$(1 - F)r^2 + Fr$	r
	p	q	r	1

Inbreeding is a property of the mating system and has nothing to do with the number of alleles at a locus. Although the examples above are in terms of A and a, the reasoning may be generalized to any number of alleles. For example, if there are three, with frequencies p, q, r, the genotypic proportions will be as shown in the lower part of Table 10-1. The correlation coefficient (between uniting gametes) for such a table is always F, no matter what arbitrary numerical values might be assigned to A_1, A_2, A_3.

Relationship between First Cousins

A person's first cousin in his parent's full sib's child, as shown in Fig. 10-1. Consider a gene X_0(A or a) of C_1. The probability that it derives from P_1 is $\frac{1}{2}$. Generally, the probability of transmission for each generation is $\frac{1}{2}$. Therefore, given a gene X_0 in C_1, the probability that his first cousin C_2 has the same gene X_0 through the line C_1-P_1-G_1-P_2-C_2 is $(\frac{1}{2})^4$ and that through the line C_1-P_1-G_2-P_2-C_2 is also $(\frac{1}{2})^4$. The total probability that C_2 inherits the common gene X_0 is $(\frac{1}{2})^4 + (\frac{1}{2})^4 = \frac{1}{8}$. By the same method it is seen that the probability that P_1 and P_2 share the same gene X_0 is $(\frac{1}{2})^2 + (\frac{1}{2})^2 = \frac{1}{2}$. Hence, the routes through grandparents G_1 and G_2 may be bypassed, and the probability that first cousins C_1 and C_2 share a common gene through the line C_1-P_1-P_2-C_2 is $(\frac{1}{2})^3 = \frac{1}{8}$. Either way, it is a fundamental genetic fact that first cousins have a probability of $\frac{1}{8}$ of sharing an identical gene by descent.

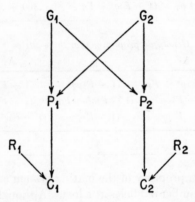

FIG. 10-1. Relationship between first cousins C_1 and C_2. The parents P_1 and P_2 are full sibs from grandparents G_1 and G_2. The other two parents R_1 and R_2 are random (unrelated) individuals.

The relationship between first cousins may be considered from another viewpoint. Using the method of conditional probabilities (Table 3-4), we see that when the genotype of one cousin is given, the probabilities for various genotypes of the other cousin (Li and Sacks, 1954) are given by

$$\text{TST} = \text{T}^3 = \tfrac{1}{4}\text{T} + \tfrac{3}{4}\text{O}$$

Writing out the nine elements and multiplying the first, second, and third rows by p^2, $2pq$, q^2, respectively, we obtain the frequencies of the various types of cousin pairs in a random-mating population, as shown in Table 10-2. If we assign the values 2, 1, 0,

TABLE 10-2. FREQUENCY OF FIRST COUSIN PAIRS IN A
RANDOM-MATING POPULATION

	AA	Aa	aa	Total
AA	$\frac{1}{4}p^3(1 + 3p)$	$\frac{1}{4}p^2q(1 + 6p)$	$\frac{1}{4}q^2(3p^2)$	p^2
Aa	$\frac{1}{4}p^2q(1 + 6p)$	$\frac{1}{4}pq(1 + 12pq)$	$\frac{1}{4}pq^2(1 + 6q)$	$2pq$
aa	$\frac{1}{4}p^2(3q^2)$	$\frac{1}{4}pq^2(1 + 6p)$	$\frac{1}{4}q^3(1 + 3q)$	q^2
Total	p^2	$2pq$	q^2	1

to genotypes AA, Aa, aa, the correlation coefficient between first
cousins will be found to be $\frac{1}{8}$. This is evident from the conditional
probabilities $\frac{1}{4}T + \frac{3}{4}O$, of which the T component yields a
correlation of $\frac{1}{2}$ and the O component, zero.

The fact that the probability of sharing a common gene derived
from Fig. 10-1 and the correlation between genotypes derived
from Table 10-2 are both $\frac{1}{8}$ apparently shows that these two
approaches are equivalent. It may be so for autosomal genes,
which are symmetrical for both sexes. For sex-linked genes, however, these two approaches are not equivalent. For example, if it
is given that a male has the gene X_0, the probability that his
sister also has it is $\frac{1}{2}$. If it is given that a female has the gene X_0,
the probability that her brother also has it is $\frac{1}{4}$. The correlation
coefficient between brothers and sisters is neither $\frac{1}{2}$ nor $\frac{1}{4}$ but
$\sqrt{\frac{1}{2} \times \frac{1}{4}} = 1/\sqrt{8} = .35355$.

The correlation between two relatives is called the *coefficient of
relationship*. It measures the degree of genetic relationship. Thus,
first cousins in a random-mating population have a coefficient of
relationship of $\frac{1}{8}$. This has nothing to do with inbreeding; it
merely says that they are related to that degree.

Children of First Cousin Parents

If two first cousins marry and have children, we say there is
inbreeding. Consider any gamete X_0 produced by C_1. Since $\frac{1}{8}$ of
the time his cousin will be of the constitution X_0X_i, where X_i is an
unrelated gene, the probability that C_1's X_0 gamete will unite
with an identical gamete is $\frac{1}{16}$ and with an unrelated gamete
is $\frac{15}{16}$. Consequently, the probabilities that the child from first

cousin parents will be AA, Aa, aa are:

$$^{15}\!/_{16}(p^2, 2pq, q^2) + \frac{1}{16}(p, 0, q)$$

That is,

$$
\begin{aligned}
\text{AA:} & \quad ^{15}\!/_{16}\, p^2 + \frac{1}{16}\, p = p^2 + \frac{1}{16}\, pq = D_I \\
\text{Aa:} & \quad ^{15}\!/_{16}\, 2pq = 2pq - \frac{2}{16}\, pq = H_I \\
\text{aa:} & \quad ^{15}\!/_{16}\, q^2 + \frac{1}{16}\, q = q^2 + \frac{1}{16}\, pq = R_I
\end{aligned}
$$

Comparing these genotypic proportions with those given in Table 10-1, we see that the inbreeding coefficient for the children from cousin marriages is $F = \frac{1}{16}$. In general, for marriages between relatives:

Inbreeding coeff of child = $\frac{1}{2}$(relationship coeff of parents)

The primary genetic effect of cousin marriages is to increase the proportion of AA and aa by an amount $\frac{1}{16}\, pq$ each, at the expense of the heterozygotes. The comparison of D_I, H_I, R_I with D_0, H_0, R_0 at various levels of gene frequencies is given in Table 10-3, where $D_0 = p^2$, $H_0 = 2pq$, $R_0 = q^2$ are the genotypic pro-

TABLE 10-3. GENOTYPIC PROPORTIONS WITH AND WITHOUT INBREEDING

Gene frequency	Children from Random Parents			$\frac{1}{16}\, pq$	Children from First Cousin Parents			R_I/R_0
	D_0	H_0	R_0		D_I	H_I	R_I	
$q = .40$	.3600	.4800	.1600	.0150	.3750	.4500	.1750	1.09
$q = .20$	.6400	.3200	.0400	.0100	.6500	.3000	.0500	1.25
$q = .10$	.8100	.1800	.0100	.005625	.815625	.168750	.015625	1.56
$q = .04$	.9216	.0768	.0016	.0024	.9240	.0720	.0040	2.50
$q = .02$	.9604	.0392	.0004	.001225	.961625	.036750	.001625	4.06
$q = .01$	.9801	.0198	.0001	.000619	.980719	.018562	.000719	7.19
$q = .00316$	.993690	.006300	.000010	.000197	.993887	.005906	.000207	20.70

portions for random mating. It is seen that, when the gene frequencies are intermediate, the effect of cousin marriage is very small. For instance, when $q = .20$, the proportion of homozygotes is increased only by the amount $pq/16 = .01$, so there will be 5 per cent recessives among the children from first cousin parents in comparison with 4 per cent from unrelated parents. The ratio $R_I/R_0 = \frac{5}{4} = 1.25$. When q is small, however, the ratio R_I/R_0 becomes large; that is, there will be several times as many recessives from first cousin marriages as those from unrelated parents. If the recessive genotype represents a *rare* hereditary disease, then its incidence among children of first cousin marriages will be several times higher than among children of ordinary families. The ratio is:

$$\frac{R_I}{R_0} = \frac{q^2 + \frac{1}{16}pq}{q^2} = \frac{1 + 15q}{16\,q}$$

This is the "harmful effect" of cousin marriages. It should be noted that the absolute amount by which the homozygote proportion is increased through inbreeding actually decreases with gene frequency, as shown in the middle column of Table 10-3. But, the value of $R_0 = q^2$ decreases much faster than $pq/16$, so the latter becomes the major component of the frequency of rare recessives.

When a much greater proportion of recessives is observed among the children of first cousin marriages, the reader must not think that the recessive gene frequency is higher among such children than among others. It is not so. The gene frequency is the same for both groups of children. The higher incidence of recessives is entirely due to the association or correlation between uniting gametes; and there is no increase in gene frequency.

Cousin Marriages in Population

Frequency of cousin marriages in a population varies widely in time as well as in space. The frequency is presumably higher in small isolated communities than in urban districts, and it is probably decreasing in the present century. In most societies the frequency of first cousin marriages is of the order of 0.5 to 2 per cent and the frequency of other types of consanguinity is probably even less (Freire-Maia, 1952; Larson, 1956; Frota-Pessoa, 1957; Alström, 1958).

Let c be the frequency of first cousin marriages in the population and $1 - c$ the frequency of random mating, where c is of the order of .01, say. Then R_0 and R_I may be thought of as the conditional probabilities for having a recessive child, given that the parents are unrelated or first cousins, respectively. Hence the general population may be reconstructed as follows:

	Cousin parents	Unrelated parents	Total
Recessives	cR_I	$(1 - c) R_0$	$R_0 + c(R_I - R_0)$
Dominants	$c(1 - R_I)$	$(1 - c)(1 - R_0)$	$1 - R_0 - c(R_I - R_0)$
Total	c	$1 - c$	1.00

Note that this setup is exactly analogous to the table on p. 99, and hence the methodology described in that section (Chap. 6, The True Rates) is also applicable to inbreeding problems. Here, $R_I = q^2 + Fpq = R_0 + Fpq$, so $R_I - R_0 = Fpq = \frac{1}{16} pq$, and the total proportion of recessives in the population is $R_0 + cFpq$. For instance, when $q = .01$, the increase in recessives due to 1 per cent ($c = .01$) first cousin marriages is $cFpq = .000006$, so there will be 106 instead of 100 recessives per million persons in the general population, although the recessives have been increased more than seven times among the children of first cousin marriages (Table 10-3). It follows that the effect of cousin marriages may be important for individual families but is negligible for the population as a whole.

It is also clear that, for very rare recessives, a considerable proportion of their parents will be first cousins. The general expression for this proportion is, from the table above,

$$c_r = \frac{cR_I}{R_0 + c(R_I - R_0)} = \frac{c(1 + 15q)}{c + 16q - cq}$$

which is equivalent to an expression of Dahlberg (1948, p. 61). When $c = q = .01$, $c_r = .0115/.1699 = 6.77$ per cent, much higher than c. If q is very small, c_r is approximately $c/(c + 16q)$, as given by Lenz in 1919, and almost all recessives are from heterozygous parents. See Kalmus (1958, p. 96) for some empirical and tabulated theoretical values of c_r (his k).

Conversely, if the values of c and c_r are known in a collection of recessives, the gene frequency in the population may be estimated by solving the equation above; thus:

$$q = \frac{c(1 - c_r)}{16c_r - 15c - cc_r}$$

Empirical Studies of First Cousin Marriages

For any given genetic trait, although the children from cousin parents have a greater probability of being homozygous, the risk is still very small in absolute value. But it is the total risk for all genetic abnormalities that is of practical importance to the parents; and the total risk is quite appreciable and may be two or three times as large as that for children from unrelated parents. Some of the recent studies on the incidence of abnormalities among children from first cousin and unrelated parents are listed in Table 10-4. These results should give us some idea as to the total risk of cousin marriages.

The four studies listed in Table 10-4 should not be compared

TABLE 10-4. EMPIRICAL STUDIES OF FIRST-COUSIN MARRIAGES: INCIDENCE OF CONGENITAL OR GENETIC ABNORMALITIES AMONG CHILDREN

Author	Traits	First-cousin parents	Unrelated parents
Böök (1957)	Genetic abnormality	$41/218 = 18.8\%$	$13/165 = 7.9\%$
Schull (1958)	Major congenital	$48/2,846 = 1.7\%$	$651/63,796 = 1.0\%$
Slatis et al. (1958)	Abnormality	$31/192 = 16.1\%$	$16/163 = 9.8\%$
Sutter (1958)	Abnormality	$169/1,044 = 16.2\%$	$176/4,094 = 4.3\%$

directly because the investigators used different criteria to define abnormality. For instance, Böök (1957) studied abnormalities that are known to be essentially genetic in nature and thus included hemophilia, a sex-linked trait not due to homozygosis. Schull, on the other hand, concentrated on major congenital malformations, which may or may not be hereditary (although the majority of them probably are). But all four studies show the same trend: the incidence of abnormalities among children from cousin parents is higher than that among children from unrelated parents. The reader is referred to the original reports (e.g., Böök, 1957) for the many interesting details of the study.

Heredity Counseling

Parents of children with hereditary diseases have frequently been referred to human geneticists for advice by their physician, frequently an obstetrician or a pediatrician. Prospective cousin couples often like to consult a geneticist. In most cases there is not much definite to tell. Studies of empirical risks are still in a very early stage, and mode of inheritance and gene frequency (which determines the incidence of disease) are known only for a limited number of cases. For cousin couples, the total risk for all types of anomalies is more meaningful than the risk for any particular disease, and this can be answered only by large-scale studies of empirical risks. A heredity clinic, like any other clinic, encounters a great variety of problems, for which no rule of thumb can be given. However, there is one thing underlying all genetic counseling situations that has to be made very clear to all clients, and that is the probabilistic nature of heredity. (Counselors do not have to use the terminology.) The importance of understanding the nature of heredity may be illustrated by the following true example.

A boy had hemophilia, and his mother was told by a hematologist who was familiar with genetics that it was due to her and not to her husband. The mother developed a deep guilty conscience for "giving" her son the disease. The piece of genetic information is valid, but it did more harm than good to the family. Half counseling is worse than none.

The probabilistic nature of heredity can be explained on two levels. First, on the population level, the continuity of nature must be explained to the lay person, who usually does not see beyond one generation. If there is a small amount of hemophilia genes circulating in the population, somebody is bound to get it, by chance, in a random-mating population. The number of affected individuals (and the frequency of the gene) remains approximately the same from generation to generation, and the shuffling of the genes from one family to another is accomplished by the system of random mating. It is through no fault of the individual that he happens to possess a number of deleterious genes. In fact, in a random-mating population, everybody has the same chance because the child (a random event) has no choice about his parents. An explanation of this nature will get rid of the guilty conscience of parents and demolish old wives' tales.

Second, on the familial level, the probabilities $\frac{1}{2}$, $\frac{1}{4}$, and so on may be explained so that the lay person understands why no one, not even the expert, can predict anything with certainty. Heredity is so much like betting on tossing coins that no fortune teller would envy the profession of genetic counseling. Ignorant of astrology and numerology, and unable to look at the crystal of gametogenesis, the geneticist can only emphasize probability and uncertainty.

In closing, we will do well to quote a few words from one of the most experienced heredity counselors. Roberts (1959) says, "It is a new thought to many people that any couple having a child run an appreciable risk that it may be malformed in some way or other, and that if people were to be deterred by very small risks no one would ever have a child" (p. 232). Then he says, "Giving genetic advice involves much more than the assessment of risks and the quoting of chances . . . . One important point is to stress the accidental nature of what has happened . . . . One explains how we *all* carry hidden, harmful, hereditary factors, but that most of us have the luck to marry someone who carries not our own particular brand, but some other kind instead" (pp. 248–249). With respect to family history of a disease, he again says, "One can at least stress the accidental nature of the distribution of hereditary defects" (p. 250). The important psychiatric aspects of genetic counseling have been discussed by Kallmann (1956), who warned that "unguided reality enforcement is apt to create fear, anxiety, and inner tension, and not realism."

Chapter 11

Variance of Quantitative Traits

Up to now we have been dealing with traits that can be classified into qualitatively distinguishable categories, of which the various blood groups constitute the most outstanding examples. Many inherited traits, however, do not fall into clear-cut categories but are measurable in quantitative terms. Examples of the latter kind are weight, height, respiration rate, blood pressure, specific disease resistance, and longevity. There is in general no clear-cut line between qualitative and quantitative traits. Hair may be classified as coarse, medium, and thin, or it may be quantified by measuring the diameter of its cross section. Many normal and abnormal physiologic entities may either be classified into arbitrarily defined categories or be measured in quantitative biochemical terms.

The inheritance of quantitative traits in man has not been as well studied as qualitative characteristics for several reasons. First, these traits are easily influenced by environmental conditions, so the genetic picture becomes somewhat blurred. Second, these traits are usually (though not always) determined not by the alleles of one or two loci but by those of many loci, so the Mendelian type of analysis is quite inadequate. Third, the statistical tools needed to study the inheritance of such traits are sometimes quite involved (and at other times not fully developed).

In this and the next chapter we shall deal with only some of the very fundamental "laws" of quantitative inheritance, which almost rank in importance with the Mendelian and Hardy-Weinberg laws for qualitative traits.

Variance of a Metrical Trait

Analogous to the study of genotype frequencies and ratios of a qualitative trait, we now study the variance of a quantitative trait. Consider the simplest case in which the metrical character is determined by a single locus, so the measurement of individuals AA, Aa, aa is Y_2, Y_1, Y_0, respectively. In the following numerical example we take $Y_2 = 8$ units, $Y_1 = 7$, and $Y_0 = 1$. If this presentation seems too abstract, the reader may think of Y as measurement of human height in inches and suppose that AA individuals are 68 inches high, Aa are 67 inches, and aa are 61 inches. It is convenient to subtract 60 from each measurement. This operation, known as *decoding*, does not affect the variance but decreases the mean by 60 inches. In a random-mating population the distribution of height will be as follows:

Genotype:	AA	Aa	aa	*Total*
Frequency, f:	$p^2 = .36$	$2pq = .48$	$q^2 = .16$	$\Sigma f = 1$
Value, Y:	$Y_2 = 8$	$Y_1 = 7$	$Y_0 = 1$	$\Sigma fY = 6.4 = \bar{Y}$
Variance:	$\sigma_Y^2 = \Sigma fY^2 - \bar{Y}^2 = 46.72 - (6.4)^2$			$= 5.76$

The Y values (i.e., 8, 7, 1) in this simple example are determined by the genotype of the individual and thus may be referred to as the *genotypic value* and the variance σ_Y^2 as the *genotypic variance*. It should be noted here that there is a certain degree of dominance, because the heterozygote value is much closer to that of one homozygote than to the other. The environmental effect on the genotypic values will be discussed later in this chapter. If the environmental influence and the frequencies of the responsible genes remain the same from generation to generation, so will the variance of the metrical trait.

Linear Component and Dominance Deviation

For reasons that will be made clear in the next chapter it is desirable to subdivide the genotypic variance into two parts based on the statistical concept of the effect of a single gene. This subdivision is so fundamental to the later development of the subject that we shall expound it in some detail. First we shall proceed along the familiar pattern in which the linear regression is presented in statistical textbooks for easy understanding, and then we shall develop some special methods in genetical terms. Let X denote the number of A genes in a genotype; thus, $X = 2, 1, 0$

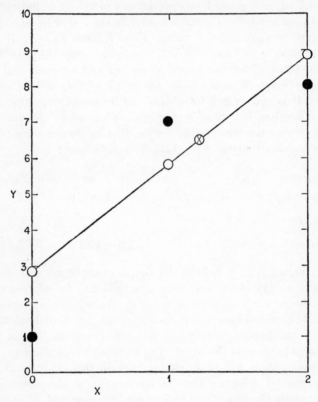

FIG. 11-1. Regression of Y (genotypic values) on X. Solid dots are actual genotypic values; circles are fitted values on the regression line. The circle with a cross is the mean point $(\bar{X}, \bar{Y})$.

for genotypes AA, Aa, aa, with frequencies p^2, $2pq$, q^2, respectively. From elementary theorems on binomial distribution, we know that $\bar{X} = 2p$ and $\sigma_X^2 = 2pq$, which the reader may readily verify. Now, the values of Y are 8, 7, 1. Our problem is to find the linear regression coefficient of Y on X, by which the variance of Y

may be subdivided into two parts. This is illustrated in Fig. 11-1, and some of the calculations are given in Table 11-1.

TABLE 11-1. COVARIANCE AND LINEAR REGRESSION

Geno-type	f	X	Y	fXY	L	D
AA	$p^2 = .36$	2	$Y_2 = 8$	$2p^2Y_2 = 5.76$	8.8	-0.8
Aa	$2pq = .48$	1	$Y_1 = 7$	$2pqY_1 = 3.36$	5.8	$+1.2$
aa	$q^2 = .16$	0	$Y_0 = 1$	$0 = 0$	2.8	-1.8
Sum...	$\Sigma f = 1.00$	....	....	$\Sigma fXY = 9.12$		
Mean..	....	$\bar{X} = 2p = 1.20$	$\bar{Y} = 6.40$	$\bar{X}\bar{Y} = 7.68$	$\bar{L} = 6.40$	$\bar{D} = 0$
(Co)-vari-ance	....	$\sigma_X^2 = 2pq = .48$	$\sigma_Y^2 = 5.76$	$\sigma_{XY} = 1.44$	$\sigma_L^2 = 4.32$	$\sigma_D^2 = 1.44$

The covariance of X and Y is defined as

$$\sigma_{XY} = \Sigma fXY - \bar{X}\bar{Y}$$

and in our numerical example it is $9.12 - 7.68 = 1.44$. From the general theory on linear regression and least squares, we know that the regression coefficient of Y on X, usually denoted by b in statistics textbooks but by α in our notation, is equal to:

$$\alpha = \frac{\sigma_{XY}}{\sigma_X^2} = \frac{1.44}{.48} = 3.0$$

which is the slope of the fitted straight line shown in Fig. 11-1. Since the fitted line passes through the point $(\bar{X}, \bar{Y}) = (1.2, 6.4)$ and we have found its slope, the position of the line is now completely determined.

The meaning of the slope $\alpha = 3$ is simple. It means (and it can be checked from the diagram) that for each unit change in X, the value of Y on the straight line will change by three units. What are the Y values on the straight line corresponding to $X = 0, 1, 2$? We need only to calculate one of the three values, because we know that their successive values differ by three units. Let L denote the Y value on the straight line. The equation of the straight line is:

$$(L - \bar{Y}) = \alpha(X - \bar{X})$$

Hence the L value corresponding to $X = 0$ is:

$$L_0 = 6.4 + 3(0 - 1.2) = 2.8$$

The other two values of L corresponding to $X = 1$ and 2 must be 5.8 and 8.8 (see right-hand part of Table 11.1). The reader should check the value $\sigma_L^2 = 4.32$ by direct calculation. The variance of these fitted values is known as the *linear component* of the genotypic variance. Its general formula, as seen from the equation of the straight line, is:

$$\sigma_L^2 = \sigma_X^2 \alpha^2 = 2pq\alpha^2$$

which, in our example, is equal to $(.48)3^2 = 4.32$.

The difference between the actual Ys and the fitted Ls, $D = Y - L$, is called the *dominance deviation*, the values of which are shown in the last column of Table 11-1. In the diagram, D represents the vertical distance from Y to the straight line. It may be verified by direct calculation that $\bar{D} = 0$ and

$$\sigma_D^2 = .36(.8)^2 + .48(1.2)^2 + .16(1.8)^2 = 1.44$$

This we shall designate the component of the genotypic variance that is due to dominance. Again, from the general theory of linear regression, we know that:

$$\sigma_Y^2 = \sigma_L^2 + \sigma_D^2$$

In our example, $5.76 = 4.32 + 1.44$. This is the very first important theorem in quantitative genetics.

Method of Successive Difference

In the previous section we have taken advantage of the known results of the general regression theory from which all our formulas follow. If we make explicit use of the binomial frequencies of X and Y, a large number of algebraic relations may be derived, of which we shall mention only one. Noting that $\bar{X} = 2p$, $\sigma_X^2 = 2pq$, and $\bar{Y} = p^2 Y_2 + 2pq Y_1 + q^2 Y_0$, we find that the regression coefficient is:

$$\alpha = \frac{\sigma_{XY}}{\sigma_X^2} = \frac{\Sigma f XY - \bar{X}\bar{Y}}{\Sigma f X^2 - \bar{X}^2} = \frac{2p^2 Y_2 + 2pq Y_1 - 2p \cdot \bar{Y}}{2pq}$$

Substituting and simplifying, we obtain:

$$\alpha = p(Y_2 - Y_1) + q(Y_1 - Y_0)$$

This shows that α is the weighted mean of the two differences $(Y_2 - Y_1)$ and $(Y_1 - Y_0)$. Regarding the latter two values as our variables and continuing the regression process once more, we find that the regression coefficient is:

$$\beta = (Y_2 - Y_1) - (Y_1 - Y_0) = Y_2 - 2Y_1 + Y_0$$

The procedure may be summarized as follows (μ for $\bar{Y}$ to achieve consistency in notation):

	f	Y	f'	Y'	f''	Y''
AA	$p^2 = .36$	$Y_2 = 8$				
			$p = .6$	$Y_2 - Y_1 = 1$		
Aa	$2pq = .48$	$Y_1 = 7$			1	$Y_2 - 2Y_1 + Y_0 = -5$
			$q = .4$	$Y_1 - Y_0 = 6$		
aa	$q^2 = .16$	$Y_0 = 1$				
Mean..	$\mu = 6.40$		$\alpha = 3.00$		$\beta = -5$	

Owing to a general theorem of Li (1957, *Biometrics* **13**:225–233; *Genetics* **42**:583–592) and the special formulas of Wright (1952), the variance of Y may be written:

$$\sigma_Y^2 = 2pq\alpha^2 + p^2q^2\beta^2$$
$$= \sigma_L^2 \quad + \sigma_D^2$$

For instance, $\sigma_D^2 = (.36)(.16)\ 5^2 = 1.44$ correctly. If we are not particularly interested in the individual magnitudes of the fitted values (L) and the dominance deviations (D) but are only interested in the two components of the genotypic variance, the routine method presented above is very expedient to achieve the desired subdivision.

It is clear that both σ_L^2 and σ_D^2 could be expressed directly in terms of p, q, and the Ys. But the value of the Ys may be expressed in various ways. For each system of writing the Ys, there is a corresponding expression for σ_L^2 and σ_D^2. Consequently, these two variance components have been given in a great variety of forms by various writers, but they are all mathematically equivalent.

Some Special Situations

The simplest and most important special case is when there is no dominance, that is, when the heterozygote value is exactly intermediate between the two homozygote values. In such a case we have $(Y_2 - Y_1) = (Y_1 - Y_0) = \alpha$ and $\beta = 0$, so:

$$\sigma_Y^2 = \sigma_L^2 = 2pq\alpha^2 \qquad \sigma_D^2 = 0$$

In words, the genotypic variance consists of the linear component only. Note that the result $\sigma_D^2 = 0$ is determined entirely by the additive property of the Y values (e.g., 2, 5, 8) and not by the gene frequencies (we ignore the trivial cases $p = 0$ or 1).

On the other extreme, we may consider a situation in which the linear component is zero. From the method of successive difference we see that $\sigma_L^2 = 0$ only when

$$\alpha = p(Y_2 - Y_1) + q(Y_1 - Y_0) = 0$$

This obtains when $Y_2 - Y_1$ and $Y_1 - Y_0$ are of opposite signs and are numerically proportional to q and p. The following is an example of this kind:

AA:	$p^2 = .36$	$Y_2 = 6$	$p = .60$	$Y_2 - Y_1 = -10$		$Y_2 - 2Y_1 + Y_0 = -25$
Aa:	$2pq = .48$	$Y_1 = 16$	$q = .40$	$Y_1 - Y_0 = \;\;\;15$		
aa:	$q^2 = .16$	$Y_0 = 1$				
Mean:		$\mu = 10$		$\alpha = 0$		$\beta = -25$

$$\sigma_Y^2 = \sigma_D^2 = p^2q^2\beta^2 = 36 \qquad \sigma_L^2 = 0$$

Note that this situation depends on both the Ys and the gene frequencies. The genotypic values 6, 16, 1, by themselves, are not sufficient to ensure $\sigma_L^2 = 0$. However, generally speaking, when the heterozygote value is greater (or smaller) than both homozygote values (overdominance), the linear component will be relatively small and the dominance component relatively large.

Complete dominance represents a special case in which
$$Y_2 - Y_1 = 0$$
and $Y_1 - Y_0 = h$ (say), so $\alpha = p \cdot 0 + qh = qh$ and $\beta = -h$ by the method of successive difference. Application of the formulas yields:
$$\sigma_L^2 = 2pq(qh)^2 = 2pq^3h^2 \qquad \sigma_D^2 = p^2q^2h^2$$
and the total genotypic variance is $\sigma_Y^2 = q^2(1 - q^2)h^2$. In this case the relative magnitude of the two components is determined entirely by the gene frequencies and is independent of the Y values. Thus, $\sigma_L^2 : \sigma_D^2 = 2pq^3 : p^2q^2 = 2q : p$. If the recessive gene is abundant (q large), the genotypic variance will consist largely in the linear component and the situation will approach that of no dominance. Conversely, if the dominant gene is abundant (p large), the genotypic variance will consist largely in the dominance component and the situation will approach that of overdominance.

Other special cases may be obtained by putting $p = q = \frac{1}{2}$, but the above three must suffice. Extensive calculations show that as long as the genotypic values form a sequence $Y_2 > Y_1 > Y_0$, the linear component will constitute a substantial portion of the genotypic variance.

The Effect of a Single Allele

The regression method is simple and meaningful when there are only two alleles. The value of α calculated previously is the average linear effect of replacing aa by Aa and that of replacing Aa by AA. In each case, one a gene is being replaced by one A gene in a genotype, and therefore α is also known as the *effect of one gene substitution*. In the more general case with multiple alleles, however, a different approach is possible (Kempthorne, 1957). The new method may be illustrated by the same numerical example we employed before, so that the relationships between the two methods may be easily seen. The population is first divided into two groups according to the alleles contained in a genotype; half the Aa individuals belong to the A group and half to the a group. The two group means (μ_1 and μ_2) are then calculated and compared with the general mean (μ) of the population. The calculations proceed as follows:

A	$Y_2 = 8$ $Y_1 = 7$ $p^2 = .36$ $pq = .24$	$\mu_1 = \dfrac{4.56}{.60} = 7.60$	$\alpha_1 = \mu_1 - \mu =$	1.2
a	$Y_1 = 7$ $Y_0 = 1$ $pq = .24$ $q^2 = .16$	$\mu_2 = \dfrac{1.84}{.40} = 4.60$	$\alpha_2 = \mu_2 - \mu =$	-1.8

$$\text{General mean:} \quad \mu = \frac{6.40}{1.00} = 6.40 \qquad \alpha_1 - \alpha_2 = \mu_1 - \mu_2 = \quad 3.0$$

The deviations α_1 and α_2 are called the *effects* of the alleles A and a, respectively. The weighted mean of these deviations is zero:

$$p\alpha_1 + q\alpha_2 = .60(1.2) + .40(-1.8) = 0$$

The fitted values of the genotypes are:

$$\text{AA:} \quad \mu + \alpha_1 + \alpha_1 = 6.4 + 1.2 + 1.2 = 8.8$$
$$\text{Aa:} \quad \mu + \alpha_1 + \alpha_2 = 6.4 + 1.2 - 1.8 = 5.8$$
$$\text{aa:} \quad \mu + \alpha_2 + \alpha_2 = 6.4 - 1.8 - 1.8 = 2.8$$

and the linear component of the genotypic variance is:

$$\sigma_L^2 = 2(p\alpha_1^2 + q\alpha_2^2) = 2(.60)(1.2)^2 + 2(.40)(1.8)^2 = 4.32$$

In the special case of two alleles, we note that $\alpha_1 - \alpha_2 = \alpha$ and the linear component is identical with $2pq\alpha^2$. The dominance component may be obtained by subtraction.

It is seen that this procedure may be extended immediately to the case of three (or more) alleles (say, A_1, A_2, A_3). The population will then be subdivided into three groups according to the common allele shared by the genotypes. The three group means μ_1, μ_2, μ_3 and their deviations α_1, α_2, α_3 are calculated. The linear component of the variance is $\sigma_L^2 = 2(p_1\alpha_1^2 + p_2\alpha_2^2 + p_3\alpha_3^2)$, where p_1 is the frequency of the allele A_1, etc. However, it should be pointed out that, whatever the number of alleles, the genotypic variance can be subdivided into only two components—the linear and the dominance—for diploid populations.

Environmental Effect on Variation

The influence of the environment is to introduce variation into the genotypic values and thus increase the variance of the population. We have assumed previously that AA individuals are of the value $Y_2 = 8$, a constant. Now suppose that the differential environmental conditions can modify the genotypic value 8 by an amount 0.6, so they increase it to 8.6 one-quarter of the time and decrease it to 7.4 one-quarter of the time. If the environmental influences act the same way for all genotypes, the true genotypic and the actual phenotypic distributions would be as follows:

Genotypes: Y		8.0			7.0			1.0	
f		.36			.48			.16	
Phenotypes: P	8.6	8.0	7.4	7.6	7.0	6.4	1.6	1.0	0.4
f	.09	.18	.09	.12	.24	.12	.04	.08	.04

With the environmental fluctuations postulated above, we see that the largest Aa individual (7.6) is actually larger than the smallest AA individual (7.4). This type of overlapping is common-place in quantitative traits. The overlapping may be slight, as it is in our example, or it may be quite extensive.

If we calculate the variance of the P values listed above, we find that $\sigma_P^2 = \Sigma f P^2 - \bar{P}^2 = 46.90 - (6.4)^2 = 5.94$ and the genotypic variance is $\sigma_Y^2 = 5.76$, as the reader may remember. The increase in variance caused by environmental influctuations is $5.94 - 5.76 = 0.18$. The latter value may be obtained independently from the variation *within* the genotypes, or simply from the distribution of the environmental effect E, viz.:

E:	+0.6	0	−0.6
f:	¼	½	¼

It will be found that $\bar{E} = 0$ and $\sigma_E^2 = 0.18$. The relation may be summarized thus:

Phenotypic		Genotypic		Environmental
σ_P^2	$=$	σ_Y^2	$+$	σ_E^2
For example, 5.94	$=$	5.76	$+$	0.18

where σ_Y^2 itself may be further subdivided into linear and dominance components, on which the environment has no influence.

It should be stressed that the subdivision of the phenotypic variance into clear-cut genotypic and environmental components is possible only when all the genotypes react the same way to a given set of environmental conditions; or, to put it in another way, the environmental influences, large or small, are independent of the genotypes. This, of course, is seldom true in nature. Indeed, each genotype may react in its own peculiar way to the same environmental agent. A satisfactory method of analysis for such interaction has yet to be developed. We should also note that, when different genotypes are exposed to different environments (e.g., AA exposed to E_1, Aa to E_2, and aa to E_3), the genetic and environmental effects are *confounded* and the variance cannot be separated at all; and we have no way to know the separate effect of either. Authoritarian opinions are of no help. This shows the extreme importance of randomization in experimental studies and random sampling in survey studies in man.

Several Pairs of Genes

Suppose that, besides the A-a pair of genes studied above, a second pair (B-b) also influences the metrical trait (height, say)

TABLE 11-2. THE COMPOUNDING OF TWO PAIRS OF GENES WITHOUT EPISTASIS IN A RANDOM-MATING POPULATION

Genotypic values	BB 5	Bb 2	bb 1	Total frequency
AA 8	13 .09	10 .18	9 .09	.36
Aa 7	12 .12	9 .24	8 .12	.48
aa 1	6 .04	3 .08	2 .04	.16
Total frequency	.25	.50	.25	1.00

so the genotypic values of BB, Bb, bb are 5, 2, 1, with frequencies .25, .50, .25, respectively. The mean genotypic value for this locus is 2.50, and by the method of successive difference we readily find that the variance is 2.25, with linear component = 2.00 and dominance component = 0.25.

Considering A-a and B-b pairs simultaneously, we obtain the joint distribution shown in the middle portion of Table 11-2, in which we assume no epistasis between the two loci; that is, the genotypic value of AABb, say, is equal to the sum of those of AA and Bb. Thus, $8 + 2 = 10$. The frequency of AABb is the product of that of AA and that of Bb; thus, $.36 \times .50 = .18$. For the distribution of the *nine* genotypes, the mean genotypic value is 8.90 and the variance (measured from this mean) is 8.01. The reader should verify these calculations before he proceeds. The results may be summarized as follows:

Source	Mean	Variance	L component	D component
A-a	6.40	5.76	4.32	1.44
B-b	2.50	2.25	2.00	0.25
Both	8.90	8.01	6.32	1.69

We note that the mean and variance of the compounded population are equal to the sum of the means and variances of the two contributing pairs calculated separately for each pair. This is always the case when the effects of the two loci are additive (no epistasis) and when the two pairs of genes are combined at random, as they are in a random-mating population at equilibrium (Chap. 8). In studying the variance, it is more convenient to take the population mean (for each pair of genes separately as well as for the compounded population) as zero, but in the above example we use some hypothetical genotypic values for ease of understanding.

The variance of the compounded population (8.01) may also be regarded as consisting of two components: the linear component is *defined* as the sum of the two linear components for the separate pairs and the dominance component as the sum of the two separate dominance components. Thus, $4.32 + 2.00 = 6.32$ is defined as the linear component and $1.44 + 0.25 = 1.69$ as the dominance component of the compounded variance 8.01. Similarly, if a third pair of genes is also involved in determining the metrical trait, the variance and its components contributed by this pair will simply be added to those for the first two pairs, as long as the genes are randomly combined and there is no epistasis; and so for the fourth pair, and so on. When we see the situation for two pairs of genes, we see the situation for several pairs.

It is due to the additivity of the variance that in the next chapter we may investigate the correlation between relatives (with respect to height, say) on the basis of one pair of genes only. For instance, if on the basis of one pair of genes the ratio

$$\frac{\sigma_L^2}{\sigma_Y^2} = \frac{4.32}{5.76} = 0.750$$

appears in a certain formulation, then in considering two pairs of genes, that ratio is simply replaced by $6.32/8.01 = .789$ in the same formulation. In other words, we may simply let σ_L^2 acquire a new meaning to denote the total linear component and σ_Y^2 the compounded genotypic variance. Then the formulation that applies to one pair of genes will also apply to any arbitrary number of genes. In the latter case, the value of σ_L^2/σ_Y^2 is the average ratio of the linear component to the genotypic variance for the several pairs of genes involved.

Chapter 12

Correlation between Relatives

In this chapter we shall deal with the correlation between close relatives with respect to a certain metrical trait (e.g., height) that is partially determined by genetic factors. The reader will soon discover that such correlations may take a wide range of values, depending upon not only the gene frequencies, but also upon the relationship between the genotypic values (Y) and the genotype (X) as well as on the environmental influences.

Parent-Offspring Correlation

The joint distribution of parent-offspring pairs in a random-mating population was given earlier in Table 3-5, which, for the convenience of calculation, is reproduced in Table 12-1, in

TABLE 12-1. CORRELATION BETWEEN PARENT AND OFFSPRING IN A RANDOM-MATING POPULATION WITH $p = .60$ AND $q = .40$

Offspring	Parent $Y = 8$, $X = 2$	$Y = 7$, $X = 1$	$Y = 1$, $X = 0$	Total
Y' X' 8 2	$p^3 = .216$	$p^2q = .144$	0	$p^2 = .360$
7 1	$p^2q = .144$	$pq = .240$	$pq^2 = .096$	$2pq = .480$
1 0	0	$pq^2 = .096$	$q^3 = .064$	$q^2 = .160$
Total	$p^2 = .360$	$2pq = .480$	$q^2 = .160$	1.00

which $X = 2, 1, 0$ take the place of the genotypes AA, Aa, aa, respectively. The corresponding genotypic values are, as in the previous chapter, taken as $Y = 8, 7, 1$, which is the measurement of the metrical trait under consideration. We wish to know the correlation between the parental Y and the offspring Y' values. Before developing a general formula or discussing the details, it is best to ignore the X values and find the coefficient of correlation between the Ys directly by straightforward numerical calculation. The marginal Y distributions for the parent and the offspring are the same, with mean $\bar{Y} = \bar{Y}' = 6.40$ and variance $\sigma_Y^2 = \sigma_{Y'}^2 = 5.76$. The covariance between the parental Y and the offspring Y' is:

$$\sigma_{YY'} = (.216)8^2 + 2(.144)8.7 + (.240)7^2 + 2(.096)7.1 + (.064)1^2$$
$$- (6.4)^2$$
$$= 43.12 - 40.96 = 2.16 = \tfrac{1}{2}(4.32) = \tfrac{1}{2}\sigma_L^2$$

and hence the correlation coefficient between Y and Y' is:

$$r_{YY'} = \frac{\sigma_{YY'}}{\sigma_Y^2} = \frac{2.16}{5.76} = .375$$

and in general, $r_{YY'} = \tfrac{1}{2}\dfrac{\sigma_L^2}{\sigma_Y^2}$

The numerical results need no comments. As to the general expression, the only relationship we have to establish is that:

$$\sigma_{YY'} = \tfrac{1}{2}\sigma_L^2$$

This may be seen by writing the covariance out algebraically:

$$\sigma_{YY'} = p^3 Y_2^2 + 2p^2 q Y_2 Y_1 + pq Y_1^2 + 2pq^2 Y_1 Y_0 + q^3 Y_0^2 - \bar{Y}^2$$

Substituting $\bar{Y} = p^2 Y_2 + 2pq Y_1 + q^2 Y_0$ and simplifying (with the aid of some simple manipulations), the expression reduces to:

$$\sigma_{YY'} = pq[p(Y_2 - Y_1) + q(Y_1 - Y_0)]^2 = pq\alpha^2 = \tfrac{1}{2}\sigma_L^2$$

Thus we have established the general formula for parent-offspring correlation. It is this relationship that prompts us to study the linear component of the genotypic variance in the preceding chapter. The larger (proportionally speaking) the linear component, the higher the parent-offspring correlation. When there is no dominance and the genotypic values form an arithmetic progression (e.g., 2, 5, 8) so the genotypic variance is all linear ($\sigma_Y^2 = \sigma_L^2$ and $\sigma_D^2 = 0$), the parent-offspring correlation is $r = \frac{1}{2}$, which is the highest value it can attain. On the other hand, if $\sigma_L^2 = 0$ and $\sigma_Y^2 = \sigma_D^2$, the parent-offspring correlation is zero. The reader should convince himself by numerical calculation that this is actually the case when $Y = 6, 16, 1$, with frequencies .36, .48, .16. With incomplete dominance, the correlation is between 0 and $\frac{1}{2}$, depending on the degree of dominance as well as the gene frequencies.

Three Steps in Parent-Offspring Correlation

The correlation formula $r = \frac{1}{2}\sigma_L^2/\sigma_Y^2$ may be viewed otherwise. That the Y values (genotypic measurements) of parent and offspring are correlated is due to the fact that their X values (or genotypes) are correlated and that the value of X determines that of Y. Let us then first find the correlation between the parental X and offspring X' from Table 12-1. The marginal distributions are the same with mean $\bar{X} = \bar{X}' = 2p$ and variance $\sigma_X^2 = \sigma_{X'}^2 = 2pq$. The covariance is:

$$\sigma_{XX'} = p^3(2 \cdot 2) + 2p^2q(2 \cdot 1) + pq(1 \cdot 1) - (2p)^2 = pq$$

so the correlation between the Xs of parent and offspring is:

$$r_{XX'} = \frac{\sigma_{XX'}}{\sigma_X^2} = \frac{pq}{2pq} = \frac{1}{2}$$

independent of the gene frequencies. The correlation between X and Y is readily found by using the established results of the preceding chapter. Recalling that $\alpha = \sigma_{XY}/\sigma_X^2$ and $\sigma_L^2 = \alpha^2\sigma_X^2$, we see that:

$$r_{XY} = \frac{\sigma_{XY}}{\sigma_X \sigma_Y} = \frac{\alpha\sigma_X^2}{\sigma_X \sigma_Y} = \frac{\alpha\sigma_X}{\sigma_Y} = \frac{\sigma_L}{\sigma_Y}$$

The correlation between the offspring X' and Y' is, of course, the same. Hence the correlation between Y and Y' consists of three steps:

$$r_{YY'} = r_{XY}\, r_{XX'}\, r_{X'Y'} = \frac{\sigma_L}{\sigma_Y} \cdot \frac{1}{2} \cdot \frac{\sigma_L}{\sigma_Y}$$

as illustrated in Fig. 12-1. The reader will find the diagrammatic representation of the formula very instructive. The correlation between the two end results (Y and Y') is equal to the product of the three correlations along the line of connection or "path" Y—X—X'—Y'. The concept that a correlation may consist in various steps or "factors" was first conceived by Fisher (1918). The only difference between his original representation and ours is that he uses the L values directly ("representative linear quantities") instead of our X. But the L values (e.g., 2.8, 5.8, 8.8) and the X values (0, 1, 2) differ only in origin and in units of $\alpha = 3$ and thus have unity correlation. Hence $r_{YX} = r_{YL}$ and $r_{XX'} = r_{LL'}$, and the two methods are equivalent.

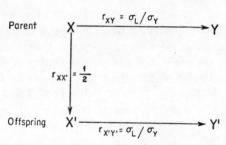

FIG. 12-1. The three steps in the correlation between parental Y and offspring Y'. They are connected through X and X'.

The correlation $r_{XX'} = \frac{1}{2}$ is intrinsic to Mendelism and panmixia and is independent of genotypic values and the gene frequencies in the population. It is one of the most basic laws in population genetics. The genotypic values (Y) can only influence the factor $r_{YX} = \sigma_L/\sigma_Y$; they have nothing whatsoever to do with the correlation $r_{XX'}$, which expresses the basic genotypic relationship between a parent and his child.

Polygenes: Environmental Influence

If the metrical trait is controlled by a number of loci, each of which acts independently (i.e., additively and no epistasis), the parent-offspring correlation remains of the form $r = \frac{1}{2}\sigma_L^2/\sigma_Y^2$, where σ_L^2 now stands for the sum of linear variance components of the various loci involved and σ_Y^2 is the sum of the genotypic variance contributed by each locus. Suppose that we observe a correlation of 0.375 between father and son in height; we would say that the average proportion of the genotypic variance that is linear is $2r = 2(.375) = .750$, assuming no epistasis.

Random environmental influences do not affect the covariance between parent and offspring, but the phenotypic variance of the metrical trait will be increased to $\sigma_P^2 = \sigma_Y^2 + \sigma_E^2$, as shown in the preceding chapter. Hence the correlation will be decreased to $\frac{1}{2}\sigma_L^2/\sigma_P^2$.

Table 12-2 gives an example of the father-son correlation in height. The original table of Pearson and Lee (1903) is given in 1-inch intervals, but it is condensed into 3-inch intervals here for

TABLE 12-2. CORRELATION BETWEEN HEIGHT OF FATHER AND SON*

Height of son, inches	Height of father, inches						Total
	60	63	66	69	72	74.5	
61	1	3	3	...	...	...	7
64	7	32	64	17	1	...	121
67	6	59	182	135	29	...	411
70	1	17	108	190	64	5	385
73	...	1	18	60	51	4	134
76	...	...	...	7	9	1	17
78.5	...	...	...	2	1	...	3
Total	15	112	375	411	155	10	1,078

* Modified from Karl Pearson and Alice Lee (1903). *Biometrika* **2**: 415. Also see Yule and Kendall (1950), p. 202.

simplicity. Thus, the class limits of the 60-inch class for the father are 58.5 and 61.5 inches. The last class, however, has a 2-inch interval, 73.5 to 75.5, with mid-value 74.5. A similar situation exists for the son. Calculation from Table 12-2 yields $r = .49$, whereas the correlation coefficient from the more detailed original table is $r = .51$. Human height is undoubtedly controlled by many loci as well as by environmental factors. It is a remarkable fact that the father-son correlation turns out to be so close to $\frac{1}{2}$, which is the theoretical value if there is no dominance or epistasis. What is more remarkable is that this empirical result was observed before the general theory of correlation between relatives was developed.

Correlation between Full Sibs

The joint distribution for two full sibs (children from the same two parents) has been given early in Chap. 3. To calculate the correlation coefficient between two full sibs with respect to the metrical trait, we assign the value Y_2 to genotype AA, etc., and then proceed as usual, obtaining first the covariance of the two full sibs. To simplify the algebra, we note that the joint distribution for full sibs may be split into the following three components (see Table 3-4) of sizes $\frac{1}{4}$, $\frac{1}{2}$, and $\frac{1}{4}$.

	Y_2	Y_1	Y_0
Y_2	p_2		
Y_1		$2pq$	
Y_0			q^2

$$\frac{1}{4}$$

	Y_2	Y_1	Y_0
Y_2	p^3	p^2q	
Y_1	p^2q	pq	pq^2
Y_0		pq^2	q^3

$$\frac{1}{2}$$

	Y_2	Y_1	Y_0
Y_2	p^4	$2p^3q$	p^2q^2
Y_1	$2p^3q$	$4p^2q^2$	$2pq^3$
Y_0	p^2q^2	$2pq^3$	q^4

$$\frac{1}{4}$$

The marginal distribution for each component is p^2, $2pq$, q^2, with variance σ_Y^2. In the first component the covariance is the same as the variance, i.e., $\text{cov} = \sigma_Y^2 = \sigma_L^2 + \sigma_D^2$. The second component is identical with the joint distribution for parent and offspring; hence the covariance, as we have learned before, is $\text{cov} = \frac{1}{2}\sigma_L^2$. In the third component the covariance is zero on account of the independence of the distribution. Therefore the total covariance is:

$$\sigma_{YY} = \frac{1}{4}(\sigma_L^2 + \sigma_D^2) + \frac{1}{2}(\frac{1}{2}\sigma_L^2) = \frac{1}{2}\sigma_L^2 + \frac{1}{4}\sigma_D^2$$

and the correlation between two full sibs in their genotypic value is:

$$r_{YY} = \frac{\sigma_{YY}}{\sigma_Y^2} = \frac{1}{2}\frac{\sigma_L^2}{\sigma_Y^2} + \frac{1}{4}\frac{\sigma_D^2}{\sigma_Y^2}$$
$$= \frac{1}{4} + \frac{1}{4}\frac{\sigma_L^2}{\sigma_Y^2}$$

The sib-sib correlation is always higher than the parent-offspring correlation by an amount of $\sigma_D^2/4\sigma_Y^2$ and has a minimum value of $\frac{1}{4}$, whatever the genotypic values. When there is no dominance ($\sigma_L^2 = \sigma_Y^2$ and $\sigma_D^2 = 0$), the correlation becomes $r = \frac{1}{4} + \frac{1}{4} = \frac{1}{2}$, the same as the parent-offspring correlation without dominance. This is, of course, the correlation between the X values (or the L values) of the two full sibs.

If the siblings are raised under a common environmental condition, the observed sib-sib correlation will be higher than that prescribed by the formula above by an amount that may be denoted by C^2. The symbol C is adopted to signify the common environmental effect, to be distinguished from the random (uncorrelated) environmental effect E.

Correlation between Parents and Children

In human genetic studies, when all the members of a family unit (two parents and their children) are examined and measured, an over-all correlation between the two parents, on the one hand, and the s children, on the other, may also be calculated. This is done by taking the total measurement of the two parents (or the mean, known as the *mid-parent*) as one variable and the total (or mean) of the s offspring as the other variable. If the gene effects are all linear (no dominance), the correlation coefficients take very simple numerical values and are independent of gene frequencies. They are summarized as follows (for proof see Li, 1954. *Am. J. Human Genet.* **6**:384):

	Number of Children in Family				
	1	2	3	4	s
One parent	$r = \sqrt{\frac{1}{4}}$	$r = \sqrt{\frac{2}{6}}$	$r = \sqrt{\frac{3}{8}}$	$r = \sqrt{\frac{4}{10}}$	$r = \sqrt{\dfrac{s}{2(s+1)}}$
Two parents	$r = \sqrt{\frac{1}{2}}$	$r = \sqrt{\frac{2}{3}}$	$r = \sqrt{\frac{3}{4}}$	$r = \sqrt{\frac{4}{5}}$	$r = \sqrt{\dfrac{s}{s+1}}$

Note that the correlation between one parent and one child is $r = \sqrt{\frac{1}{4}} = \frac{1}{2}$ in the absence of dominance; this is the case we studied in the first two sections of this chapter. Also note that the correlation with one known parent increases with the number of children and approaches $\sqrt{1/2} = .707$ as a limit as $s \to \infty$. But, $\sqrt{1/2}$ is the correlation between two known parents and one child. This shows that one additional known parent is worth a large number of children in correlation studies. The minimum correlation with two known parents is higher than the maximum correlation with one known parent.

When there is dominance, the situation is slightly more complicated. We shall examine two cases as examples. The correlation between two parents and one child is now $\sqrt{1/2} \cdot \sigma_L^2/\sigma_Y^2$. As to the correlation between two parents and two children, we note that the variance of the total of two full sibs is:

$$\sigma_Y^2 + \sigma_Y^2 + 2\sigma_{YY} = 2\sigma_Y^2 + 2(\tfrac{1}{2}\sigma_L^2 + \tfrac{1}{4}\sigma_D^2)$$

so the correlation coefficient is:

$$r = \frac{2\sigma_L^2}{\sqrt{2\,\sigma_Y^2}\,\sqrt{2\sigma_Y^2 + \sigma_L^2 + \tfrac{1}{2}\,\sigma_D^2}}$$

This value is only slightly higher than $\sqrt{2/3} \cdot \sigma_L^2/\sigma_Y^2$ if the dominance component is small.

Correlation between Other Relatives

In genetic studies the correlations between immediate family members are by far the most important ones, as the correlation between other relatives decreases very rapidly with the distance of the relationship. In the following we shall give the correlations of only a few types of common relatives.

Relatives, in the genetic sense, are persons who have one or more common ancestors and may therefore share common genes. Ordinarily, husband and wife are *not* relatives, although both are related to their children. The in-laws, socially regarded as close relatives, are not genetically related at all. For our purpose, the relatives may be broadly classified into two types. One is *bilineal;* that is, the two individuals are related through both parents. The only common example of this type in human population is full brothers and sisters who are connected through the common father as well as through the common mother. This we have already studied. Double first cousins also belong to this type, but they are so rare in our population that we will not discuss them here. Another type of relative is *unilineal;* that is, the two individuals are connected through only one parent. The great

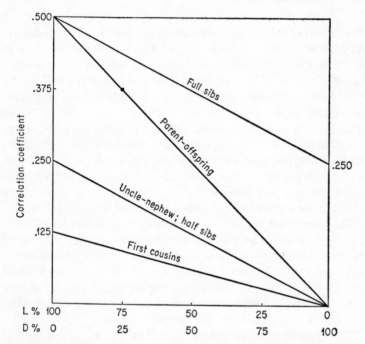

FIG. 12-2. Correlation between close relatives in a random-mating population. The dot indicates parent-offspring $r = .375$ from data of Table 12-1 and calculations on p. 196.

majority of relatives belong to this type. For instance, your uncle is *either* your mother's brother *or* your father's brother. The correlation between such relatives may be obtained in a simple manner. It is simply the correlation between their X values multiplied by σ_L^2/σ_Y^2. The correlation for the X values is $\frac{1}{2}$ for each parent-offspring step or from one sib to another, as we have learned in previous sections. Without going into the details, we list the correlations between some common relatives as follows:

$$\left.\begin{array}{l}\text{Grandparent and grandchild}\\ \text{Half brothers and sisters}\\ \text{Uncle (aunt) and nephew (niece)}\end{array}\right\} \quad r = \tfrac{1}{4}\frac{\sigma_L^2}{\sigma_Y^2}$$

$$\text{First cousins} \qquad\qquad\qquad r = \tfrac{1}{8}\frac{\sigma_L^2}{\sigma_Y^2}$$

The values of the correlation coefficients between these relatives vary with the linear component of the genotypic variance, as shown in Fig. 12-2. The corresponding correlation values for sex-linked genes may be found by matrix method (Li and Sacks, 1954). A method of separating the autosomal from the sex-linked component of the genotypic variance has been given by Reeve (1953). Since in man there are 22 pairs of autosomes of varying length and 1 pair of sex chromosomes, the sex-linked component of the genotypic variance is probably very small (of the order of, say, 1 to 5 per cent). Any common environmental influence between the relatives will increase the correlation between them, although we explicitly emphasized this point only for full sibs.

The correlation between an unrelated husband and wife is not genetic in nature, and is due to either assortative mating or common environmental factors, depending on the nature of the trait under consideration. Comparing this with the parent-child and sib-sib correlations would provide us with a rough estimate of the relative importance of environmental and hereditary influences with respect to specified traits.

The genetics of quantitative traits has now become a field of its own and should become more and more important in human genetics. An excellent general introduction to this subject is that of Falconer (1960), which should be consulted by all interested students.

References

Aird, I., Bentall, H. H., Mehigen, J. A., and Roberts, J. A. F. (1954). The blood groups in relation to peptic ulceration and carcinoma of colon, rectum, breast and bronchus: Association between ABO blood groups and peptic ulceration. *Brit. Med. J.* **2**:315–321.

Allison, A. C. (1954a). Protection afforded by sickle cell trait against subtertian malarial infection. *Brit. Med. J.* **1**:290–292.

Allison, A. C. (1954b). Notes on sickle cell polymorphism. *Ann. Human Genet.* **19**:39–57.

Alström, C. H. (1958). First cousin marriages in Sweden 1750–1844. *Acta Genet. et Statist. Med.* **8**:295–369.

Bailey, N. T. J. (1951). The estimation of the frequencies of recessives with incomplete multiple selection. *Ann. Eugenics* **16**:215–222.

Beet, E. A. (1949). The genetics of the sickle cell trait in a Bantu tribe. *Ann. Eugenics* **14**:279–284.

Böök, J. A. (1957). Genetical investigations in a north Swedish population. The offspring of first-cousin marriages. *Ann. Human Genet.* **21**:191–221; Penrose's note, pp. 222-223.

Boyd, W. C. (1950). *Genetics and the Races of Man.* Little, Brown & Company, Boston.

Boyd, W. C. (1954). Maximum likelihood method for estimation of gene frequencies from MNS data. *Am. J. Human Genet.* **6**:1–10; corrections in vol. 7, p. 444.

Boyd, W. C. (1956). Variances of gene frequency estimates. *Am. J. Human Genet.* **8**:24–38.

Buckwalter, J. A., Wohlwend, E. B., Colter, D. C., Tidrick, R. T., and Knowler, L. A. (1956). Peptic ulceration and ABO blood groups. *J.A.M.A.* **162**:1215-1220.

Ceppellini, R. (1955). Discussion on polymorphism in man. *Cold Spring Harbor Symposia Quant. Biol.* **20**:252–255.

Ceppellini, R., Siniscalco, M., and Smith, C. A. B. (1955). The estimation of gene frequencies in a random mating population. *Ann. Human Genet.* **20**:97–115.

Chu, E. H. Y., and Giles, N. H. (1959). Human chromosome complements in normal somatic cells in culture. *Am. J. Human Genet.* **11**:63–79.

Clarke, C. A. (1959). Correlations of ABO blood groups with peptic ulcer, cancer, and other diseases. *J. Med. Educ.* **34**:400.

Clarke, C. A., Finn, R., McConnell, R. B., and Sheppard, P. M. (1958). The protection afforded by ABO incompatibility against erythroblastosis due to Rhesus anti-D. *Intern. Arch. Allergy Appl. Immunol.* **13**:380.

Cornfield, J. (1951). A method of estimating comparative rates from clinical data: Applications to cancer of the lung, breast, and cervix. *J. Natl. Cancer Inst.* **11**:1269-1275.

Cotterman, C. W. (1947). A weighting system for the estimation of gene frequencies from family records. Contributions of Laboratory of Vertebrate Zoology, University of Michigan, no. 33, pp. 1-21.

Crow, J. F. (1958). Some possibilities for measuring selection intensities in man. *Human Biology* **30**:1-13.

Dahlberg, G. (1948). *Mathematical Methods for Population Genetics.* Interscience Publishers, Inc., New York.

DeGroot, M. H. (1956). Efficiency of gene frequency estimates for the ABO system. *Am. J. Human. Genet.* **8**:39-43.

DeGroot, M. H., and Li, C. C. (1960). Simplified method of estimating the MNS gene frequencies. *Ann. Human Genet.* **24**:109-115.

Dobzhansky, T. (1955). *Evolution, Genetics, and Man.* John Wiley & Sons, Inc., New York. Chapman & Hall, Ltd., London.

Dunn, L. C. (1953). Variations in the segregation ratio as causes of variations in gene frequency. *Acta Genet. et. Statist. Med.* **4**:139-147.

Dunn, L. C. (1959). *Heredity and Evolution in Human Populations.* Harvard University Press, Cambridge, Mass.

Falconer, D. S. (1960). *Introduction to Quantitative Genetics.* Ronald Press, New York.

Finney, D. J. (1948). The estimation of gene frequencies from family records: I. Factors without dominance; II. Factors with dominance. *Heredity* **2**:199-215; 369-389.

Finney, D. J. (1949). The truncated binomial distribution. *Ann. Eugenics* **14**:319-328.

Fisher, R. A. (1918). The correlation between relatives on the supposition of mendelian inheritance. *Trans. Roy. Soc. Edinburgh* **52**:399-433.

Fisher, R. A. (1934). The effect of methods of ascertainment upon the estimation of frequencies. *Ann. Eugenics* **6**:13-25.

Fisher, R. A. (1940). The estimation of the proportion of recessives from tests carried out on a sample not wholly unrelated. *Ann. Eugenics* **10**:160-170.

Ford, C. E. (1960). Human cytogenetics: Its present place and future possibilities. *Am. J. Human Genet.* **12**:104-117.

Ford, C. E., and Hamerton, J. L. (1956). The chromosomes of man. *Nature* (London) **178**:1020-1023.

Fraccaro, M., Kaijser, K., and Lindsten, J. (1959). Chromosome complement in parents of patients with gonadal dysgenesis (Turner's syndrome). *Lancet* **2**:1090.

Freire-Maia, N. (1952). Frequencies of consanguineous marriages in Brazilian populations. *Am. J. Human Genet.* **4**:194-203.

Frota-Pessoa, O. (1957). The estimation of the size of isolates based on census data. *Am. J. Human Genet.* **9**:9-16.

Glass, H. B. (1950). The action of selection on the principal Rh alleles. *Am. J. Human Genet.* **2**:269-278.

Glass, H. B., and Li, C. C. (1953). The dynamics of racial intermixture: An analysis based on the American Negro. *Am. J. Human Genet.* **5**:1-20.

Haldane, J. B. S. (1932). A method for investigating recessive characters in man. *J. Genet.* **25**:251–255.

Haldane, J. B. S. (1937). The effect of variation on fitness. *Am. Naturalist* **71**:337–349.

Haldane, J. B. S. (1938). The estimation of the frequencies of recessive conditions in man. *Ann. Eugenics* **8**:255–262.

Haldane, J. B. S. (1939). The equilibrium between mutation and random extinction. *Ann. Eugenics* **9**:400–405.

Haldane, J. B. S. (1940). The conflict between selection and mutation of harmful recessive genes. *Ann. Eugenics* **10**:417–421.

Haldane, J. B. S. (1947). The dysgenic effect of induced recessive mutations. *Ann. Eugenics* **14**:35–43.

Haldane, J. B. S. (1949). Parental and fraternal correlations for fitness. *Ann. Eugenics* **14**:288–292.

Haldane, J. B. S. (1956). The estimation and significance of the logarithm of a ratio of frequencies. *Ann. Human Genet.* **20**:309–311.

Haldane, J. B. S., and Moshinsky, P. (1939). Inbreeding in Mendelian populations with special reference to human cousin marriage. *Ann. Eugenics* **9**:321–340.

Harris, H. (1959). *Human Biochemical Genetics.* Cambridge University Press, New York.

Hogben, L. (1946). *An Introduction to Mathematical Genetics.* W. W. Norton & Company, Inc., New York.

Hsia, D. Y-Y. (1959). *Inborn Errors of Metabolism.* Year Book Publishers, Inc., Chicago.

Hsu, T. C. (1961). Chromosomal evolution in cell populations. *International Rev. Cytology* (in press).

Jameson, R. J., Lawler, S. D., and Renwick, J. H. (1956). Nail-patella syndrome: Clinical and linkage data on family G. *Ann. Human Genet.* **20**:348–353.

Kallmann, F. J. (1956). Psychiatric aspects of genetic counseling. *Am. J. Human Genet.* **8**:97–101.

Kalmus, H. (1958). *Variation and Heredity.* Routledge & Kegan Paul, Ltd., London.

Kempthorne, O. (1957). *An Introduction to Genetic Statistics.* John Wiley & Sons, Inc., New York.

Larson, C. A. (1956). The frequency of first cousin marriages in a south Swedish rural community. *Am. J. Human Genet.* **8**:151–153.

Lehmann, H., and Raper, A. B. (1956). Maintenance of high sickling rate in an African community. *Brit. Med. J.* **1**:333–336.

Lejeune, J. (1958). Sur une solution "a priori" de la methode "a posteriori" de Haldane. *Biometrics* **14**:513–520.

Lejeune, J., Gautier, M., and Turpin, R. (1959a). Les chromosomes humaines en culture de tissus. *Compt. rend. acad. sci.* **248**:602–603.

Lejeune, J., Gautier, M., and Turpin, R. (1959b). Études des chromosomes somatique de neuf enfants mongolien. *Compt. rend. acad. sci.* **248**:1721–1722.

Levene, H. (1949). On a matching problem arising in genetics. *Ann. Math. Stat.* **20**:91–94.

Levene, H. (1953). Genetic equilibrium when more than one ecological niche is available. *Am. Naturalist* **87**:331–333.

Levene, H. (1956). Selection genetics in man. *Ann. N.Y. Acad. Sci.* **65**:3–11.

Levine, P. (1943). Serological factors as possible causes in spontaneous abortions. *J. Heredity* **34**:71–80.

Lewis, J. H., and Li, C. C. (1958). Genetic considerations in hemophilia A and B. *Proc. Intern. Congr. Genet.* **10**:168.

Lewontin, R. C. (1953). The effect of compensation on populations subject to natural selection. *Am. Naturalist* **87**:375–381.

Lewontin, R. C. (1958). A general method for investigating the equilibrium of gene frequency in a population. *Genetics* **43**:419–434.

Li, C. C. (1953a). Is Rh facing a crossroad? A critique of the compensation effect. *Am. Naturalist* **87**:257–261.

Li, C. C. (1953b). Some general properties of recessive inheritance. *Am. J. Human Genet.* **5**:269–279.

Li, C. C. (1954). Some methods of studying human genetics: I. Segregation of recessive offspring; II. The severity of an abnormality; III. Methods for establishing the genetic role; IV. Linkage versus association. *Methods in Med. Research* **6**:1–38.

Li, C. C. (1955a). *Population Genetics.* University of Chicago Press, Chicago.

Li, C. C. (1955b). The stability of an equilibrium and the average fitness of a population. *Am. Naturalist* **89**:281–296.

Li, C. C. (1956a). The concept of path coefficient and its impact on population genetics. *Biometrics* **12**:190–210.

Li, C. C. (1956b). The components of sampling variance of ABO gene frequency estimates. *Am. J. Human Genet.* **8**:133–137.

Li, C. C. (1959). Notes on relative fitness of genotypes that forms a geometric progression. *Evolution* **13**:564–567.

Li, C. C. (1960). A diagrammatic representation of the proportions of genotypes and phenotypes in a panmictic population. *Ann. Human Genet.* **24**:117–119.

Li, C. C. (1961). Genetical-epidemiological methods—a synthesis. *Ann. N. Y. Acad. Sci.* **91**:806–812.

Li, C. C., and Sacks, L. (1954). The derivation of joint distribution and correlation between relatives by the use of stochastic matrices. *Biometrics* **10**:347–360.

Mather, K. (1951). *The Measurement of Linkage in Heredity.* Methuen & Co., Ltd., London.

Matsunaga, E., and Itoh, S. (1958). Blood groups and fertility in a Japanese population, with special reference to intrauterine selection due to maternal-foetal incompatibility. *Ann. Human Genet.* **22**:111–131.

McConnell, R. B. (1956). Selection and the ABO blood group locus. *Ann. N.Y. Acad. Sci.* **65**:12–25.

McKusick, V. A., and collaborators (1960). Medical genetics 1958 and 1959. *J. Chronic Diseases* **10**:255–363; **12**:1–202. (Catalogue and review of current literature.)

Medawar, P. B. (1959). *The future of man.* Basic Books, Inc., New York.

Morton, N. E. (1955). Sequential tests for the detection of linkage. *Am. J. Human Genet.* **7**:277–318.

Morton, N. E. (1957). Further scoring types in sequential linkage tests with a critical review of autosomal and partial sex-linkage in man. *Am. J. Human Genet.* **9**:55–75.

Morton, N. E. (1959). Genetic tests under incomplete ascertainment. *Am. J. Human Genet.* **11**:1–16.

Morton, N. E. (1960). The mutational load due to detrimental genes in man. *Am. J. Human Genet.* **12**:348–364.

Mourant, A. E. (1954). *The Distribution of the Human Blood Groups.* Basil Blackwell & Mott, Ltd., Oxford; Charles C Thomas, Publisher, Springfield, Ill.

Muller, H. J. (1950). Our load of mutations. *Am. J. Human Genet.* **2**:111–176.

Neel, J. V. (1949). The inheritance of sickle cell anemia. *Science* **110**:64–66.

Neel, J. V. (1951). The inheritance of the sickling phenomenon, with particular reference to sickle cell disease. *Blood* **6**:389–412.

Neel, J. V. (1956). The genetics of human hemoglobin differences: Problems and perspectives. *Ann. Human Genet.* **21**:1–30.

Neel, J. V., and Schull, W. J. (1954). *Human Heredity.* University of Chicago Press, Chicago.

Osborne, R. H., and DeGeorge, F. V. (1959). *Genetic Basis of Morphological Variation.* Harvard University Press, Cambridge, Mass.

Owen, A. R. G. (1953). A genetical system admitting of two distinct stable equilibria under natural selection. *Heredity* **7**:97–102.

Penrose, L. S. (1935). The detection of autosomal linkage in data which consist of pairs of brothers and sisters of unspecified parentage. *Ann. Eugenics* **6**:133–138.

Penrose, L. S. (1946). A further note on the sib-pair linkage method. *Ann. Eugenics* **13**:25–29.

Penrose, L. S. (1954). *The Biology of Mental Defect.* Sidgwick & Jackson, Ltd., London.

Penrose, L. S. (1959). *Outline of Human Genetics.* John Wiley, & Sons, Inc., New York.

Prout, T. (1953). Some effects of variations in the segregation ratio and of selection on the frequency of alleles under random mating. *Acta. Genet. et Statist. Med.* **4**:148–151.

Race, R. R., and Sanger, R. (1954). *Blood Groups in Man.* Charles C Thomas, Publisher, Springfield, Ill.

Ranney, H. M. (1954). Observations on the inheritance of sickle-cell hemoglobin and Hemoglobin C. *J. Clin. Invest.* **33**:1634–1641.

Reed, S. C. (1955). *Counseling in Medical Genetics.* W. B. Saunders Company, Philadelphia.

Reed, T. E. (1959). The definition of relative fitness of individuals with specific genetic traits. *Am. J. Human Genet.* **11**:137–155.

Reeve, E. C. R. (1953). Studies in quantitative inheritance: III. Heritability and genetic correlation in progeny tests using different mating systems. *J. Genet.* **51**:520–542.

Renwick, J. H., and Lawler, S. D. (1955). Genetical linkage between the ABO and nail-patella loci. *Ann. Human Genet.* **19**:312–331.

Rife, D. C. (1951). A method for testing two-factor inheritance. *J. Heredity* **42**:162.

Roberts, J. A. F. (1957). Blood groups and susceptibility to disease: A review. *Brit. J. Prevent. & Social Med.* **11**:107–125.

Roberts, J. A. F. (1959). *An Introduction to Medical Genetics,* Oxford University Press, New York.

210 HUMAN GENETICS: PRINCIPLES AND METHODS

Schiff, F., and Verschuer, O. von (1933). Serologische Untersuchungen an Zwillingen. *Ztschr. f. Morphol. u. Anthropol.* **32**:244–249.

Schull, W. J. (1958). Empirical risks in consanguineous marriages: sex ratio, malformation, and viability. *Am. J. Human Genet.* **10**:294–343.

Sheppard, P. M. (1959). Natural selection and some polymorphic characters in man. In D. F. Roberts and G. A. Harrison (eds.), *Natural Selection in Human Populations.* Pergamon Press, New York.

Sjögren, T. (1943). Klinische und erbbiologische Untersuchungen über die Heredo-ataxien. *Acta Psychiat. et Neurol.* Suppl. 27. Copenhagen: E. Munksgaard.

Slatis, H. M. (1954). A method of estimating the frequency of abnormal autosomal recessive genes in man. *Am. J. Human Genet.* **6**:412–418.

Slatis, H. M., Reis, R. H., and Hoene, R. E. (1958). Consanguineous marriages in the Chicago region. *Am. J. Human Genet.* **10**:446–464.

Smith, C. A. B. (1953). The detection of linkage in human genetics. *J. Roy. Stat. Soc.* **B15**:153–192.

Smith, C. A. B. (1954). *Biomathematics.* Hafner Publishing Company, New York.

Smith, C. A. B. (1956). A test for segregation ratios in family data. *Ann. Human Genet.* **20**:257–265.

Smith, C. A. B. (1957). Counting methods in genetical statistics. *Ann. Human Genet.* **21**:254–276.

Smith, C. A. B. (1959). A note on the effects of method of ascertainment on segregation ratios. *Ann. Human Genet.* **23**:311–323.

Smithies, O., and Walker, N. F. (1955). Genetic control of some serum proteins in normal humans. *Nature* (London) **176**:1265.

Snyder, L. H. (1932). Studies in human inheritance IX. The inheritance of taste deficiency in man. *Ohio J. Sci.* **32**:436–440.

Snyder, L. H. (1934). Studies in human inheritance X. A table to determine the proportion of recessives to be expected in various matings involving a unit character. *Genetics* **19**:1–17.

Snyder, L. H., and David, P. (1959). *The Principles of Heredity.* D. C. Heath & Company, Boston.

Steinberg, A. G. (1959). Methodology in human genetics. *J. Med. Educ.* **34**:315–334.

Stern, C. (1943). The Hardy-Weinberg law. *Science* **97**:137–138.

Stern, C. (1960). *Principles of Human Genetics.* W. H. Freeman, San Francisco.

Stevens, W. L. (1938). Estimation of blood-group gene frequencies. *Ann. Eugenics* **8**:362–375.

Sutter, J. (1958). Recherches sur les effets de la consanguinité chez l'homme. Declume Press, Lons-le-Saunier.

Sutton, H. E., Neel, J. V., Livingstone, F. B., Binson, G., Kunstadter, P., and Trombley, L. E. (1959). The frequencies of haptoglobin types in five populations. *Ann. Human Genet.* **23**:175–183.

Tjio, J. H., and Levan, A. (1956). The chromosome number of man. *Hereditas* **42**:1–6.

Vogel, F. (1959). Moderne Probleme der Humangenetik. *Ergeb. inn. Med. u. Kinderheilk.* **12**:52.

Wiener, A. S. (1943). *Blood Groups and Transfusion.* Charles C Thomas, Publisher, Springfield, Ill.

Wiener, A. S., and Wexler, I. B. (1958). *Heredity of the Blood Groups.* Grune & Stratton, Inc., New York.

Wilson, E. B. (1951). Note on association of attributes. *Proc. Natl. Acad. Sci.* **37**:696–704.

Woolf, B. (1955). On estimating the relation between blood group and disease. *Ann. Human Genet.* **19**:251–253.

Wright, S. (1951). The genetical structure of populations. *Ann. Eugenics* **15**:323–354.

Wright, S. (1952). The genetics of quantitative variability. In E. C. R. Reeve and C. H. Waddington (eds.), *Quantitative Inheritance.* H.M.S.O., London.

Yule, G. U., and Kendall, M. D. (1950). *An Introduction to the Theory of Statistics.* Hafner Publishing Company, New York.

Index